THE FRICK COLLECTION

VOLUME IV · SCULPTURE

COURT · THE FRICK COLLECTION

THE
FRICK COLLECTION

AN ILLUSTRATED CATALOGUE

VOLUME IV · SCULPTURE

German, Netherlandish,
French and British

THE FRICK COLLECTION · NEW YORK · 1970

DISTRIBUTED BY PRINCETON UNIVERSITY PRESS

TABLE OF CONTENTS

GERMAN, NETHERLANDISH AND FRENCH SCULPTURE

Fifteenth Through Seventeenth Centuries

JOHN POPE-HENNESSY assisted by ANTHONY F. RADCLIFFE

FRENCH AND BRITISH SCULPTURE

Eighteenth and Nineteenth Centuries

TERENCE W. I. HODGKINSON

UNIDENTIFIED SCULPTURE

INDICES

GERMAN, NETHERLANDISH AND FRENCH SCULPTURE

Fifteenth Through Seventeenth Centuries

HANS MULTSCHER, Attributed to

c. 1400–1467

Born about 1400, Multscher was active as a sculptor at Ulm by 1427. His earliest known work, the stone Karg altar in the Minster at Ulm, is dated 1433. Between 1456 and 1458 he was engaged on his masterpiece, an altar for the Frauenkirche at Sterzing (Vipiteno). It is widely assumed that in his formative years Multscher visited the Netherlands, and Flemish influences play an important part in his later works both in painting and in sculpture. Multscher's documented sculpture is exclusively in wood and stone, and the bronze bust discussed below is the only cast sculpture with which he has been credited. He died at Ulm in 1467.

Reliquary Bust of a Female Saint (16.2.59)

Bronze: H. 12⅝ in. (32 cm).

Description: The head, represented in full-face, is inclined slightly to the spectator's right. The eyelids are lowered, and the pupils are indicated by small circular depressions. The hair, which is bound with a circlet incised with a punched scroll-work pattern, falls loose over the shoulders and down the back. The plain robe has a flat collar incised with parallel strokes, and falls in front in four radiating folds. Below the throat is a large Lombardic κ. The lower edge of the bust is decorated with an incised scroll border corresponding with that on the circlet, interrupted in the center at the front and back and beneath the right shoulder by quatrefoils in relief (cast separately); the quatrefoil beneath the left shoulder is missing. On the top of the head is a rectangular opening for relics, measuring $2^3/_8 \times 1^9/_{16}$ in. (6×4 cm), with a hinge on the right-hand side.

Condition: Dark brass-like bronze, with dark brown flecks (apparently of discoloration rather than patination), and traces of gilding on the hair, the circlet, the collar of the robe, and the incised lower border. The tip of the nose is dented. In the three surviving quatrefoils the lower lobe is absent; the missing lobes may have been attached with dowels to the original base. The missing hinged lid was perhaps of crystal.

There is no record of the reliquary bust prior to 1910, when it was published by Bode[1] as a work by Veit Stoss. This implausible attribution seems to have been based on the Polish provenance of the bust (see below) and on supposed analogies

3

with wooden sculptures by Veit Stoss at Cracow. The attribution to Stoss was retained when the bust was exhibited with other works from the Pierpont Morgan collection in London and New York. There is no evidence that Veit Stoss worked in bronze. The bust is described by Bode as "the only German bust in bronze of this date at present known"; the putative date to which this sentence refers would have been around 1500–33. The ascription is rejected by Maclagan[2] with the comment that "it seems more probable that it is the work of an artist in the Netherlands, and that it dates from the fifteenth century. The ornamental details, like the general type of the bust, would be difficult to parallel in German art, while it does suggest the Low Countries."

In 1940 a case was stated by Weinberger[3] for ascribing the bust to the Swabian sculptor Hans Multscher. The ascription rests on analogies with the wooden sculpture on the Multscher altar at Sterzing, especially with the drapery folds of the St. Ursula and the type of the St. Barbara. According to this theory, the bust would be contemporary with the Sterzing altar (1456–58). Since no work in bronze by Multscher is known, this explanation of the authorship of the bust is conjectural; it is, however, accepted by Müller,[4] who notes[5] convincing resemblances to a wooden *Virgin and Child* by Multscher at Landsberg. There is some evidence, summarized by Weinberger and Müller, for the practice of bronze casting in South Germany in the mid-fifteenth century—works habitually cited in this connection are the tombs of Conrad von Weinberg and Anna von Hohenlohe at Schöntal and the bronze retable of 1447 in the choir of the Cathedral at Augsburg—but it is generally recognized that the present bust postulates close contact with Netherlandish bronze sculpture of the second quarter of the fifteenth century. Weinberger in particular observes that "the technical treatment of the Frick bust seems to reveal an acquaintance with similar work in the Netherlands." The bust is accepted as a work of Multscher by Tripps.[6]

According to Maclagan, "the initial κ may or may not indicate that Saint Katherine is represented," while according to Weinberger "it may indicate the name of the Saint (Katherine?), but might just as well stand for the name of a donor, a church, or a monastery." The editors of *The Frick Collection Catalogue*[7] suggest that the bust may represent "Saint Catherine (Katherine) of Sweden, whose cult was widely popular in the north of Europe during the fifteenth century… although the saints Catherine of Siena and of Alexandria must be men-

4

tioned as remoter possibilities." In the absence of a Dominican habit the candidature of St. Catherine of Siena may safely be ruled out, and the balance of probability is that the bust represents St. Catherine of Alexandria. It is described as "a bust of St. Catherine" by Müller, who, however, suggests[8] that the letter κ may indicate a connection with King Casimir IV of Poland (1447–92).

Exhibited: London, Victoria and Albert Museum, 1910–12, No. 1419, lent by J. Pierpont Morgan. New York, Metropolitan Museum, Morgan Collection, 1914–16, No. 1581, lent by the J. Pierpont Morgan Estate.

Collections: Said to have come from a wooden church at Zamosc (Western Galicia) destroyed in the first half of the nineteenth century. Sold through Durlacher Bros., February 22, 1910, to J. Pierpont Morgan, London and New York. Duveen. Frick, 1916.

NOTES

1 W. Bode, *Collection of J. Pierpont Morgan: Bronzes of the Renaissance and Subsequent Periods,* Paris, 1910, I, p. xl, II, p. 27, No. 206, Pls. CXLII, CXLIII.
2 E. Maclagan, in *The Frick Collection Catalogue,* VI, 1954, pp. 54–55.
3 M. Weinberger, "A Bronze Bust by Hans Multscher," *Art Bulletin,* XXII, 1940, pp. 186–89.
4 C. T. Müller, *Sculpture in the Netherlands, Germany, France and Spain: 1400–1500,* London, 1966, pp. 74–75, Pl. 86(A).
5 Verbal communication.
6 M. Tripps, *Hans Multscher: Seine Ulmer Schaffenszeit 1427–1467,* Augsburg, 1969, p. 268, No. 19.
7 *Loc. cit.*
8 Verbal communication.

NUREMBERG

First Half of the Sixteenth Century

Paris (16.2.7)

Bronze: H. to top of figure 10½ in. (26.6 cm); H. to top of staff 10¾ in. (27.4 cm); H. of base 3/16 in. (4 mm).

Description: A naked youth is shown with head turned in profile over his left shoulder. His left hand, holding an apple, rests against his hip, and in his right hand he holds a long staff or crook which is curved at the top and fits at the bottom into a hole in the base. His hair is tied with a ribbon, and the conventionalized musculature of his throat, chest, and abdomen is strongly marked. The figure is cast solid, in one with a shallow circular base with a molded rim.

Condition: Medium reddish-brown bronze. Flecks of gilding on the interior of the right arm and more extensive traces of gilding on the hair and apple suggest that the whole figure was originally gilt. Though the staff or crook is cast separately, it appears also to have been gilt, and is therefore likely to be original.

The bronze is the finest surviving example of a model widely associated with and almost certainly deriving from Antonio Pollajuolo. An inferior version, lacking the staff and mounted on a circular molded base of greater depth than that of the present example, is in the Musée Jacquemart-André, Paris, and a lead statuette, almost identical in pose but somewhat different in the facial type, is in Berlin.[1] A poor variant of the present model is in the Albertinum at Dresden,[2] and another, coarsely worked and supported by a tree trunk behind the ankles, was in the A. von Frey collection, Paris (No. 135). Much inferior, seemingly modern versions of the figure exist in the Victoria and Albert Museum, London (A. 2–1929), and the Baltimore Museum of Art (Sadie A. May Collection). Each of the latter figures has a pendant in the form of a *Venus Pudica* with elaborately dressed hair holding a mirror in the right hand. The Baltimore bronzes were purchased in Paris from Daguerre, and are apparently identical with a pair of statuettes sold in 1892 with the collection of Madame d'Yvon,[3] described as "imitation allemande d'un bronze italien."

Though it was ascribed by Molinier in the Mannheim catalogue (see below) to the workshop of Verrocchio and was given at the Royal Academy exhibition in

8

1904 to the School of Verrocchio, the present bronze has invariably been connected in the more recent literature with Pollajuolo. The attribution was first advanced by Bode,[4] who seems to have assumed that the *Paris* was adapted from the Berlin lead figure (conjecturally a *Hercules*) and that the discrepancies in modelling of the two works reflected a difference in typology. The ascription to Pollajuolo is accepted by Schottmüller,[5] by Planiscig,[6] who mistakenly describes the bronze as "conosciuto da due esemplari," and, with reserve, by Van Marle,[7] who calls it "very close to the master himself." The figure is rejected by Weinberger,[8] and is listed by Sabatini[9] among works wrongly ascribed to Antonio Pollajuolo, with the comment that "stilisticamente stanno tra Bertoldo e il Pollajuolo. Di quest'ultimo non hanno l'energia lineare nè la finezza dei bronzetti originali. Sembrano di un imitatore forse fiorentino." The attribution is also contested in a confused note by Ortolani.[10] Maclagan[11] concludes that "it is perhaps safest to leave this beautiful bronze under the name which has become traditional now, although with some hesitation; for it is at least possible that its actual origin should be looked for north of Florence even if it is directly based on a figure by Pollaiuolo." The editors of *The Frick Collection Catalogue*[12] draw attention to resemblances between the bronze and drawings by or from the following of Pollajuolo. The Dresden bronze has been incorrectly given to Francesco da Sant'Agata.[13]

There is no demonstrable connection between the handling of the bronze in The Frick Collection and that of the autograph small bronzes of Antonio Pollajuolo. The resemblance noted in *The Frick Collection Catalogue* to two drawings ascribed to the School of Antonio Pollajuolo in the Musée Bonnat at Bayonne[14] is superficial, but the style of Antonio Pollajuolo is strongly recalled both in the type and in the pose. The assumption that the Frick bronze is of Italian origin is not necessarily correct, since the version at Dresden is certainly, and that in the Musée Jacquemart-André is probably, a German casting. Analogies for the two bronzes in London are sought by Maclagan[15] in works by Peter Vischer the Younger. The female figure which accompanies the *Paris* in the groups in London and Baltimore depends from a Venus type of which the best example is the so-called *Amerbach Venus* in the Historisches Museum at Basel, but the style of hairdressing in both bronzes is characteristically German. If the two *Venus* statuettes reproduce a lost original, this was undoubtedly a German bronze. It is possible that the Frick *Paris* was originally accompanied by a *Venus* figure of this or a related type.

The closest point of reference for the present figure in German bronze sculpture is provided by the reliefs from the *Fugger Grille*[16] from the Rathaus at Nuremberg, now at the Château de Montrottier near Annecy, which are conjecturally given by Meller[17] to Hermann Vischer the Younger.

Exhibited: London, Victoria and Albert Museum, 1901–12, No. 134, lent by J. Pierpont Morgan. London, Royal Academy, Winter Exhibition, 1904, Case A (No. 2), lent by J. Pierpont Morgan.[18] London, Burlington Fine Arts Club, Italian Sculpture and other Plastic Art of the Renaissance, 1912, No. 54, lent by J. Pierpont Morgan.[19] New York, Metropolitan Museum, Morgan Collection, 1914–16, No. 1407, lent by the J. Pierpont Morgan Estate.

Collections: Charles Mannheim, Paris.[20] Sold privately to J. Pierpont Morgan, London and New York. Duveen. Frick, 1916.

NOTES

1 For these two bronzes see W. Bode, *The Italian Bronze Statuettes of the Renaissance,* I, London, 1907, Pl. XVII.

2 H. 10¹/₁₆ in. (25.5 cm). *Staatliche Kunstsammlungen Dresden: Bildwerke der Renaissance und des Barocks,* Dresden, 1965, p. 263, No. B11, Inv. No. 2V 3132, as "Paduanisch um 1520: Nachbildung einer Statuette des Antonio Pollaiuolo."

3 May 30–June 4, 1892, Galerie Georges Petit, Paris, p. 59, Lots 273, 274.

4 W. Bode, *Denkmäler der Renaissance-Skulptur Toskanas,* Berlin, 1892–1905, text vol., p. 177; *The Italian Bronze Statuettes,* I, p. 17, Pl. XVII; *Die italienischen Bronzestatuetten der Renaissance,* Berlin, 1922, pp. 19–20; *Collection of J. Pierpont Morgan: Bronzes of the Renaissance and Subsequent Periods,* Paris, 1910, I, pp. viii–ix, 5, No. 14, Pl. XI.

5 F. Schottmüller, in Thieme-Becker, *Allgemeines Lexikon der bildenden Künstler,* XXVII, Leipzig, 1933, p. 213.

6 L. Planiscig, *Piccoli bronzi italiani del rinascimento,* Milan, 1930, p. 7, Pl. XVIII, Fig. 25.

7 R. van Marle, *The Development of the Italian Schools of Painting,* XI, The Hague, 1929, p. 447.

8 M. Weinberger, review of Planiscig's *Piccoli bronzi italiani,* in *Zeitschrift für bildende Kunst,* LXV, 1931–32, Beilage, p. 53, as North Italian.

9 A. Sabatini, *Antonio e Piero del Pollajuolo,* Florence, 1944, pp. 98–99.

10 S. Ortolani, *Il Pollaiuolo,* Milan, 1948, p. 165.

11 E. Maclagan, in *The Frick Collection Catalogue,* V, 1953, p. 13.

12 *Loc. cit.*

13 *Bode-Museum Berlin: Italienische Bronzen der Renaissance und des Barock,* 1967, p. 13, No. 24.

14 J. Bean, *Les Dessins italiens de la Collection Bonnat,* Paris, 1960, Nos. 120, 121.

15 E. Maclagan, in *Victoria and Albert Mu-*

seum: *Review of the Principal Acquisitions,* London, 1929, pp. 7–8.

16 For a full account of which see H. Stafski, *Der Jüngere Peter Vischer,* Nuremberg, 1962, pp. 47–48.

17 S. Meller, *Peter Vischer der Aeltere und seine Werkstatt,* Leipzig, 1925, pp. 157–63.

18 *Illustrated Catalogue of a Collection of Italian Sculpture and other Plastic Art of the Renaissance,* London, 1913, p. 76, No. 54.

19 *Collection Charles Mannheim: Objets d'art,* ed. É. Molinier, Paris, 1898, p. 40, No. 134, Pl. 1.

20 *Works by the Old Masters,* London, 1904, p. 56.

NUREMBERG

Last Quarter of the Sixteenth Century

Satyr Mother with a Child Satyr (16.2.22)

Bronze: H. 10⁵/₁₆ in. (26.2 cm).

Description: The standing satyress is naked save for a ribbon round her neck and a girdle of foliage round her waist joined at the back by a satyr head. She holds out with both hands a large scallop shell, from which a child satyr, standing between her arms, is drinking. With his right hand the child grasps the handle of a ewer on the ground beside him; the face of the ewer is decorated with a satyr mask. Beside the satyress' left leg is a reclining goat, and at the front of the naturalistic base is a quiver with its strap looped over a tree stump. Among the details on the base are two snakes, a frog, and a lizard.

Condition: Thin greenish-brown patina over yellowish bronze.

No other example of this beautiful group is known. Though the bronze was accepted as a work of Riccio by Bode,[1] initially with some reserve, and by Planiscig,[2] it is relegated by Maclagan[3] to a place "among the productions of Riccio's workshop rather than as an example of his own skill." Two models by Riccio of a *Satyress and Child Satyr* are known. In one of these, which exists in autograph versions in the Museo Nazionale, Florence (formerly in the Estensische Kunstsammlung, Vienna),[4] and in the collection of Mrs. Arthur Goodhart, New York,[5] the child clings with both hands to the left knee of the satyress. In the other model, which is known only through workshop versions,[6] the child stands at its mother's side. In both cases the linking of the two figures is characteristic of Riccio's compositional procedure, and diverges markedly from the present bronze, which is conceived with two main lateral views. The head of the satyress is compared by Planiscig with that of the terracotta *St. Agnes* in S. Canziano at Padua[7] and with a terracotta *Virgin and Child* formerly in the Eduard Simon collection,[8] but is notably less classical in type than these two works or than the head of, for example, the *Abundantia* in the Museo Nazionale, Florence. For these reasons an origin in the Riccio workshop must be ruled out.

Weihrauch[9] relates the present bronze to a *Satyr* in the Victoria and Albert Museum, London (ascribed when in the Lederer collection, Vienna, to Desiderio da Firenze), and regards both statuettes as the work of an unidentified Paduan sculptor active around 1550. This grouping is incorrect. One of the most individual features of the present bronze is the base, where, as Planiscig[10] observes, "erblicken wir neben naturalistischen Pflanzen und aus der Erde hervorragenden Wurzel- stücken Reptilien, Schlangen und Eidechsen, Elemente, die der Werkstatt Riccios vom Naturabguss her geläufig sind." The analogies cited by Planiscig between the treatment of the base and that of a *Fettered Marsyas* in the Bargello have no validity, and it is probable that the bronze was produced, in the second half of the sixteenth century, in one of the Northern workshops in which naturalistic detail was extensively employed. The closest analogies for it occur in the work of Wenzel Jamnitzer (1508–85), where the top-heavy proportions of the figures, the large hands, the form of the ewer (with the decoration on its handle and lip and the satyr mask), the working on the horns and hair, and the naturalistic detail of the base find a general parallel. For the satyr mask compare particularly the masks round the vase at the top of the Merkel tablecenter (1549), formerly in the col- lection of Baron Henri de Rothschild and now in the Rijksmuseum, Amsterdam;[11] for the goat compare the Holzschuher goblet in the Germanisches Museum, Nuremberg;[12] and for other details compare the ewers in the Cathedral at Dubrov- nik[13] and in S. Maria presso S. Celso, Milan.[14] While these analogies are insuffi- cient to admit of a direct attribution to Wenzel Jamnitzer, they suggest very clearly that we have here to do with a Nuremberg bronze of the last quarter of the sixteenth century. The extended shell seems to indicate that the bronze was designed as a table decoration, perhaps as a salt.

Exhibited: London, Victoria and Albert Museum, 1901–12, No. 349, lent by J. Pier- pont Morgan. New York, Metropolitan Mu- seum, Morgan Collection, 1914–16, No. 1426, lent by the J. Pierpont Morgan Estate.

Collections: Henry Joseph Pfungst, Lon- don. Sold through Durlacher Bros., June 25, 1901, to J. Pierpont Morgan, London and New York. Duveen.[15] Frick, 1916.

NOTES

1 The first reference to the bronze by Bode occurs in a note in the Pfungst catalogue

(Descriptive catalogue of a small collection principally of XVth and XVIth century

bronzes, London, 1901, p. 8, No. 49), where it is classified as North Italian, late fifteenth century, with the proviso that "the base, the ewer and the goat appear to have been added, and the whole group re-chased at a later date." In Bode's later references to the group this proviso is omitted, and the bronze is ascribed to Riccio. For these see: W. Bode, *Collection of J. Pierpont Morgan: Bronzes of the Renaissance and Subsequent Periods,* Paris, 1910, I, p. 11, No. 35, Pl. XXVIII; *The Italian Bronze Statuettes of the Renaissance,* III, London, 1912, p. 22, Pl. CCXLIII; *Die italienischen Bronzestatuetten der Renaissance,* Berlin, 1922, Pl. 51.

2 L. Planiscig, *Andrea Riccio,* Vienna, 1927, pp. 359–60, 485, Fig. 441.

3 E. Maclagan, in *The Frick Collection Catalogue,* V, 1953, pp. 40–41.

4 Planiscig, *op. cit.,* Fig. 445.

5 See *Albright Art Gallery, Buffalo: Master Bronzes,* 1937, No. 130, Fig. 130.

6 Planiscig, *op. cit.,* Figs. 442, 443.

7 *Idem,* Fig. 146.

8 *Idem,* Figs. 287, 288.

9 H. R. Weihrauch, *Europäische Bronzestatuetten,* Brunswick, 1967, p. 115, Fig. 130.

10 Planiscig, *op. cit.,* pp. 359–60.

11 M. Rosenberg, *Jamnitzer,* Frankfurt am Main, 1920, Pl. 4.

12 Reproduced in E. Kris, "Der Stil Rustique," *Jahrbuch der Kunsthistorischen Sammlungen in Wien,* N.S. I, 1926, pp. 137–208, Fig. 121.

13 Rosenberg, *op. cit.,* Fig. 23.

14 *Idem,* Fig. 34.

15 *Duveen Sculpture in Public Collections of America,* New York, 1944, No. 181.

CASPAR GRAS

c. 1590–1674

Born probably in 1590 in Württemberg, Gras is first recorded at Innsbruck as an assistant of Hubert Gerhard at the court of the Archduke Maximilian der Deutschmeister (d. 1618). On Gerhard's departure from Innsbruck in 1613, Gras succeeded him as court sculptor, retaining this post under Archduke Leopold V. Through his work on the tomb of Maximilian der Deutschmeister and on the Leopoldsbrunnen at Innsbruck, as well as through many minor works, Gras established himself as a bronze sculptor of exceptional technical accomplishment. He died at Schwaz (Tyrol) in 1674.

Infant Faun (16.2.28)

Bronze: H. 17⅛ in. (43.5 cm).

Description: A nude child with pointed ears is shown seated on a mound, with his right leg outstretched and his left knee bent. With his extended right arm he holds out a bunch of grapes to a lizard, which climbs over his right foot. His left arm is raised behind him, forming a continuing diagonal with the right. On the irregular naturalistic base are grapes, vine leaves, and twigs.

Condition: Dark lacquer over reddish-brown bronze. There are four holes in the upper surface of the bunch of grapes and a large hole at the side of the bunch.

A second version of the bronze, formerly in the Henry Oppenheimer and Paget collections, is now in a London private collection. In this the base is somewhat deeper than in the present bronze, the grapes, vine leaves, and other detail on the base are omitted, and the lizard is differently posed. The treatment of the hair is drier and more linear than in the present example.

At the Edwardes sale (see below) the Frick bronze was catalogued as "an old Italian bronze statuette," but in the Morgan collection it appears initially to have been regarded as German and was exhibited as such in the Victoria and Albert Museum, London. The designation of the bronze as Paduan is due to Bode,[1] and is accepted by Maclagan.[2] Bode's account reads as follows: "I should also like to designate as Paduan-Venetian works of this period [*i.e.,* the second quarter of the sixteenth century] two statuettes of children of larger dimensions in the Collection.

One of them represents a young Satyr (as proved by the pointed ears which would not have been given to a youthful Bacchus) feeding a lizard with grapes. This important bronze ... is considered, in the Pierpont Morgan Collection, to be German work. If so, it must emanate from the workshop of the Vischers of Nuremberg which was markedly influenced by Padua and Venice. But apart from the fact that a *genre* figure of this size in bronze would not have been produced at that time in Germany, the type, the head and the details ... as well as the whole execution, all point to Italy, and to Padua in particular.''

The case for regarding the bronze as Paduan rests on the connection between the lizard in the Frick bronze and a number of nature-cast small bronzes conventionally ascribed to Riccio. One of the most important of these is a group of two lizards in the Bayerisches Nationalmuseum, Munich,[3] of which an imperfect version in the Kunsthistorisches Museum, Vienna, is given by Planiscig[4] to the Riccio workshop. Three related nature-casts of snakes are also in the Kunsthistorisches Museum.[5] Though nature-casts of snakes and other reptiles were employed in Padua in the early sixteenth century—they occur, for example, on the handles of a bowl by Severo da Ravenna in the Kunsthistorisches Museum[6]— there is no reason to believe that the paired lizards and the related bronzes were necessarily made at so early a date. Some cognate bronzes in the Kunstgewerbe-museum, Berlin, are associated by Pechstein[7] with the studio of Jamnitzer.

The nature-cast vine leaves and lizard on the base of the present bronze were undoubtedly produced in the same workshop as the nature-cast detail on the columns of the monument of the Archduke Maximilian der Deutschmeister in the Pfarrkirche St. Jakob at Innsbruck (1615–19). The latter were cast in the shop of Heinrich Reinhart, and were designed by Caspar Gras.[8] The casting of the present bronze, which is hollow throughout with two rods inside as supports, is extremely fine, and finds a close analogy in the *Goddess of the Chase,* the only figure on Gras' Leopoldsbrunnen at Innsbruck of which part of the interior can be seen. The figure sculpture of the Leopoldsbrunnen[9] was likewise modelled by Gras and cast by Reinhart before 1630. That the present bronze dates from about this time is corroborated by the pose of the naked figure, which, as noted by Maclagan, depends from a classical original of the type of the figures of *Hercules Strangling the Serpents* in the Museo Capitolino, Rome, and in Turin,[10] but is elaborated in a manner that would be inexplicable at any earlier time. The head of

the child is not perfectly compatible with any of the widely differing child types of the putti on the corners of the monument or the stem of the fountain, but in view of its manifest connection with the Reinhart foundry the probability that it was nonetheless modelled by Gras is very strong. The holes in the bunch of grapes seem to indicate that the figure formed part of a table fountain.

Exhibited: London, Victoria and Albert Museum, 1902–12, No. 393, lent by J. Pierpont Morgan. New York, Metropolitan Museum, Morgan Collection, 1914–16, No. 1503, lent by the J. Pierpont Morgan Estate.

Collections: Sir Henry Hope Edwardes, Bart., Wooton Hall, Ashbourne, Derbyshire. His sale, April 24–26, 1901, Christie's, Lot 211, sold for 650 guineas to Jacques Seligmann, Paris. J. Pierpont Morgan, London and New York. Duveen. Frick, 1916.

NOTES

1 W. Bode, *Collection of J. Pierpont Morgan: Bronzes of the Renaissance and Subsequent Periods,* Paris, 1910, I, pp. xxvii–xxviii, II, p. 3, No. 116, Pl. LXXX.

2 E. Maclagan, in *The Frick Collection Catalogue,* V, 1953, pp. 31–32.

3 See H. R. Weihrauch, *Die Bildwerke in Bronze und in anderen Metallen,* Munich, 1956, pp. 70–71, No. 94, as Riccio.

4 L. Planiscig, *Die Bronzeplastiken,* Vienna, 1924, p. 39, No. 62.

5 *Idem,* Nos. 59–61.

6 *Idem,* No. 58.

7 K. Pechstein, *Kataloge des Kunstgewerbemuseums Berlin, III: Bronzen und Plaketten,* Berlin, 1968, Nos. 134–38.

8 For these see E. Egg, "Caspar Gras und der Tiroler Bronzeguss des 17. Jahrhunderts," *Veröffentlichungen des Museum Ferdinandeum,* XL, 1961, pp. 30–37.

9 For which see H. R. Weihrauch, "Der Innsbrucker Brunnen des Kaspar Gras," *Pantheon,* XXXI, 1943, pp. 105–11.

10 S. Reinach, *Répertoire de la statuaire grecque et romaine,* 2nd ed., I, Paris, 1906, p. 461.

GABRIEL GRUPELLO

1644–1730

A scion of a noble Milanese family, Grupello was born in 1644 and trained in the Netherlands, where he was a pupil of Artus Quellinus in 1658–59. Practicing in Brussels after 1673, he became first sculptor of that city and principal sculptor to Charles II of Spain. His most important works were executed at Düsseldorf, to which city he was summoned by Johann Wilhelm von der Pfalz in 1695 and where he remained till his patron's death in 1716. Thereafter he was attached to the court of the Emperor Charles VI. Grupello died in 1730.

Eve (16.2.60)

Bronze: H. 19 3/16 in. (48.7 cm).

Description: The figure is represented nude, gazing slightly downwards to her left at an apple held in her outstretched left hand. With her right hand she presses against her thigh a second apple with a sprig of foliage; its leaves conceal her nakedness. Her hair is parted in the center, and one tress falls over her left shoulder and descends at the back to a point below her shoulder blade. Her right knee is bent, and her left foot is slightly advanced. The figure is cast in one with a shallow rectangular base, which is ½ in. (1.3 cm) high at the back and slightly lower at the front.

Condition: Grayish bronze patinated to golden-brown. The ankles were originally joined by an iron nail, the cut-off ends of which are visible on the outside of the right ankle and on the insides of both ankles; the outer end on the left ankle is covered with a bronze plug. There is a contemporary insertion in lighter bronze on the right cheek and the right side of the neck, and another insertion under the left buttock. The inside of the right leg and the outside of the left leg have been repaired. There are three circular plugs on the right side and three rectangular plugs on the left. On the upper surface of the left wrist are two dents.

The figure is related in reverse to the figure of Eve in Dürer's 1504 engraving of the *Fall of Man* (Bartsch No. 1), in which Eve is represented with an apple in her outstretched right hand and with a second apple with a sprig of foliage in her left. While in the Hainauer collection, the present bronze was ascribed by Bode[1] and Molinier[2] to Peter Vischer the Younger. This attribution seems to have replaced

24

an earlier attribution to Peter Vischer the Elder, and was in turn replaced by Bode[3] with a later ascription to Hans Vischer. The ascription to Peter Vischer the Younger appears to have been regarded with some scepticism by Kaemmerer,[4] who comments that "der classische Kopf mit seinem fein ciselierten Haar, die breiten Formen des Körpers weichen von den bekannten und durch die Urheber-marke beglaubigten Arbeiten dieses Künstlers einigermassen ab und lassen auf eine weiter vorgeschrittene Epoche der deutschen (?) Bildnerei schliessen, ohne dass ich einen plausibleren Namen vorzuschlagen wüsste." The bronze is accepted as a work of Hans Vischer by Meller,[5] with a dating around 1530–35, as well as by Maclagan[6] and the editors of *The Frick Collection Catalogue*.[7] Meller associates it with two statuettes of a walking youth, one, in Munich, naked, and the other, in Vienna, with nature-cast drapery. The Vienna bronze is given by Planiscig[8] to Hans Vischer. This attribution is contested by Weihrauch,[9] who assigns both bronzes, no doubt correctly, to an unidentified Nuremberg sculptor working around 1530–40. The present bronze is not by the same sculptor as these figures, nor by the author of a female figure at Copenhagen with which it is also grouped by Meller; the latter bronze is a work of Leonhard Kern.

It was first suggested by Bange[10] that the bronze was attributable to Gabriel Grupello on the strength of its affinities to a marble statue of *Galatea* at Schwet-zingen and of a reference to a bronze statuette of *Eve* ("121. Eine Statue die Eva von Metall Klein") in an inventory of the contents of Grupello's studio made in 1716. The *Eve* is accepted as a work of Grupello by Weihrauch,[11] and is claimed to have formed part of a group of the *Fall of Adam and Eve*. A seated figure of Adam (H. 17⁵/₁₆ in.; 44 cm) from a larger group of this subject is in the Kunstmuseum at Düsseldorf. The attribution to Grupello is endorsed, with a tentative dating between 1700 and 1705, by Kultermann,[12] who regards the Frick bronze as the model for the statue of the *Boeotian Atalanta* by Charasky at Schwetzingen.

The connection of the bronze with the Vischer studio cannot be seriously maintained, since its style is incompatible with, for example, the *Venus* ascribed to Georg Vischer in the Louvre.[13] The casting procedure recurs in a figure of Johann Wilhelm von der Pfalz by Grupello in the Kunstmuseum at Düsseldorf, where a circular bronze plug is visible on the right ankle and an insertion in lighter bronze occurs on the left foot,[14] and in the Düsseldorf *Minerva* and *Paris*.[15]

26

Exhibited: Berlin, Kunstgeschichtliche Gesellschaft, Kunstwerke des Mittelalters und der Renaissance, 1898, lent by Frau Julie Hainauer. London, Victoria and Albert Museum, 1906–12, No. 1204, lent by J. Pierpont Morgan. New York, Metropolitan Museum, Morgan Collection, 1914–16, No. 1578, lent by the J. Pierpont Morgan Estate.

Collections: Frédéric Spitzer, Paris.[16] Oscar Hainauer, Berlin. J. Pierpont Morgan, London and New York. Duveen. Frick, 1916.

NOTES

1 W. Bode, *Die Sammlung Oscar Hainauer,* Berlin, 1897, pp. 24, 75, No. 88, repr. p. 23.

2 É. Molinier, "La Collection Hainauer," *Gazette des Beaux-Arts,* 3e pér., XVIII, 1897, p. 501.

3 W. Bode, "Kleinbronzen der Söhne des älteren Peter Vischer," *Jahrbuch der Königlich Preuszischen Kunstsammlungen,* XXIX, 1908, p. 37; *Collection of J. Pierpont Morgan: Bronzes of the Renaissance and Subsequent Periods,* Paris, 1910, I, p. xxxix, II, p. 26, No. 203, Pl. CXXXIX.

4 L. Kaemmerer, in *Ausstellung von Kunstwerken des Mittelalters und der Renaissance aus Berliner Privatbesitz veranstaltet von der Kunstgeschichtlichen Gesellschaft,* Berlin, 1899, pp. 78–79, reproduced.

5 S. Meller, *Peter Vischer der Ältere und seine Werkstatt,* Leipzig, 1925, p. 210; *Die deutschen Bronzestatuetten der Renaissance,* Munich, 1926, p. 27, Pl. XXX.

6 E. Maclagan, in *The Frick Collection Catalogue,* VI, 1954, pp. 28–30.

7 *Loc. cit.*

8 L. Planiscig, *Die Bronzeplastiken,* Vienna, 1924, p. 192, No. 313.

9 H. R. Weihrauch, *Bayerisches Nationalmuseum: Die Bildwerke in Bronze und in anderen Metallen,* Munich, 1956, p. 24, No. 29.

10 E. F. Bange, "Eine Bronzestatuette von Gabriel Grupello," *Berliner Museen,* LV, 1934, pp. 107–09; *Die deutschen Bronzestatuetten des 16. Jahrhunderts,* Berlin, 1949, p. 27.

11 H. R. Weihrauch, *Europäische Bronzestatuetten,* Brunswick, 1967, pp. 380–82.

12 U. Kultermann, *Gabriel Grupello,* Berlin, 1968, pp. 181–82, 193, 255–56.

13 Bange, *Die deutschen Bronzestatuetten,* Fig. 72.

14 Written communication of C. Theuerkauff, 1968.

15 See R. Klapheck, "Johann Moritz von Nassaus Gartenstadt Kleve," *Jahrbuch der rheinischen Denkmalspflege,* XXIX, 1936, p. 234.

16 Not included in the Spitzer sale of 1893.

JACQUES JONGHELINCK

1530–1606

The son of a medallist and die-master, Jonghelinck was born in Antwerp in 1530. He was trained under Cornelis Floris, and in 1552 visited Italy, where he entered the workshop of Leone Leoni in Milan. Returning to the Low Countries, he was employed after 1555 on a number of official commissions, beginning with the tomb of Charles the Bold (commissioned 1558) in the church of Onze Lieve Vrouw at Bruges, and including the bust of the Duke of Alba discussed below and a related statue of the Duke. Jonghelinck was also active at Antwerp as a medallist and seal-engraver, and till his death in 1606 he enjoyed undisputed supremacy as the principal bronze sculptor in the Netherlands.

The Duke of Alba (16.2.61)

Inscribed, on the curved face of the base: FERDINAND, / ALBAE / DVX; and, on the lowest riser: IVNGELINGVS OPTIMO DVCI / 1571. Bronze: H. 45⅞ in. (116.5 cm).

Description: The Duke is represented in armor, with head turned slightly to his right. His hair is thick and curling, and his long beard flows over the linen ruff which rises above his gorget. His breastplate and paul-drons are decorated with military trophies, and below the right shoulder on the breastplate is a lance-rest. He wears the collar of the Golden Fleece, and over his left shoulder hangs a marshal's sash, the tips of which descend at the side to a point several inches below the base of the bust. The bust is cut away below the breastplate, and is cast in one with a molded base with double volutes. The eyes are deeply incised, and the hair is untouched by the chisel.

Condition: Dark lacquer over medium brown bronze.

Don Fernando Alvarez de Toledo, third Duke of Alba, was born on October 29, 1507. After taking part in the siege of Tunis (1535) and the battle of Mühlberg (1547) he commanded the Spanish army in France and Italy, and in 1567 he was sent by Philip II of Spain to the Netherlands as Viceroy and Captain General. He was recalled to Spain in 1573, and died, at the age of seventy-five, on Decem-

28

ber 11, 1582. He is remembered for the ruthless severity of his repression of heresy and nationalism in the Netherlands.

The present bust is one of a number of representations of the Duke produced by Jonghelinck during Alba's term of office in the Netherlands. Among these are two medals,[1] both, like the present work, dated 1571, the second having on the reverse an inscription related to that on the bust: OPTI / MO / PRINCI / PE / 1571. Also in 1571, a full-length statue of the Duke, cast from captured cannon and signed IVNGELINGI OPVS EX AERE CAPTIVO, was set up in the fortress at Antwerp. On the instructions of Alba's successor, Don Luis de Requezens, the statue was dismantled and buried in 1574 and destroyed in 1577.[2] An engraving made by Philip Galle before the demolition of the statue[3] shows the Duke trampling under foot Heresy and Rebellion; the elaborately decorated plinth was in part by Guillaume van den Broeck.

The present bust was known to Simonis, who reproduces it[4] with the comment: "Le buste fondu par lui, est la reproduction, à mi-corps et sans bras, du bronze triomphal. Il fut offert, par l'artiste lui-même, au gouverneur qui l'emporta, à son depart des Flandres, en 1574. Il a donné naissance à la légende, rapportée par Nagler d'après la version de Strada, qu'un double de la statue entière avait été envoyé en Espagne." Maclagan[5] likewise asserts that the bust, "except for a slight raising of the head and an alteration in the left pauldron, almost exactly reproduces the upper part of the statue." This is incorrect; not only is the pose in the statue somewhat different, but another suit of armor is shown. There is therefore no foundation for the view that the bust originated as a sectional replica of the statue and was presented by Jonghelinck to the Duke; the balance of probability is that it was commissioned by Alba, along with the statue and the medals, as an independent portrait bust. The burial of the statue was commemorated by Jonghelinck in 1574 in a further medal which has as its reverse the Fall of Icarus. The relation of the full-length statue to the allegorical statues of Leone Leoni, in whose studio Jonghelinck was trained, is analyzed by Keutner,[6] and it is rightly pointed out[7] that the present bust is also dependent on portrait busts by Leoni.

The bust[8] was presumably taken to Spain by Alba after his recall, and remained in the possession of his descendants till 1810, when it was removed by Ney (see below). In modern times it first came to notice in 1874, when it was exhibited in

30

Paris[9] and was mentioned in an article by Mantz.[10] It was later cited by Plon[11] in connection with a bust of the Duke of Alba by Leone Leoni, now in the Royal Collection at Windsor Castle. When it was again exhibited in 1913,[12] the bust was the subject of comment by Bertaux[13] and Vitry.[14]

Exhibited: Paris, Palais du Corps législatif, Exposition en faveur de l'oeuvre des Alsaciens et Lorrains, April 1874, lent by Vicomte Gustave de Reille. Paris, Hôtel de Sagan, Objets d'art du moyen-âge et de la renaissance, 1913, No. 93, lent by Baron Victor Reille.

Collections: Dukes of Alba, Madrid (till 1810). Maréchal Ney, Duc d'Elchingen, Château des Condreaux, near Châteaudun. After the execution of Ney (1815) the bust appears to have remained in the Château des Condreaux, and in 1825 it was sold with the house to Maréchal Vicomte de Reille. Vicomte Gustave de Reille, Paris. Baron Victor Reille, Paris. Duveen. Frick, 1916.

NOTES

1 For these see G. van Loon, *Histoire métallique des XVII Provinces des Pays Bas,* The Hague, I, 1732, p. 134.

2 J. Simonis, *L'Art du médailleur en Belgique,* II, Jemeppe-sur-Meuse, 1904, pp. 175–76.

3 Reproduced by E. van Meteren, *Belgische Historie van onsen tyden,* The Hague, III, 1636, fol. 67, and by H. Keutner, "Ueber die Entstehung und die Formen des Standbildes im Cinquecento," *Münchner Jahrbuch der bildenden Kunst,* dritte Folge, VII, 1956, p. 157, Fig. 17.

4 *Op. cit.,* Pl. D, pp. 136–42.

5 E. Maclagan, in *The Frick Collection Catalogue,* VI, 1954, pp. 31–33.

6 *Loc. cit.*

7 In Thieme-Becker, *Allgemeines Lexikon der bildenden Künstler,* XIX, Leipzig, 1926, pp. 135–37.

8 For which see also W. C. Mees, *Alva,* Assen, 1957, pp. 11–16.

9 *Notice sommaire des objets d'art exposés au profit de la colonisation de l'Algérie par les Alsaciens-Lorrains,* 2e sér., Paris, 1874, p. 75.

10 P. Mantz, "Exposition en faveur de l'oeuvre des Alsaciens et Lorrains," *Gazette des Beaux-Arts,* 2e pér., X, 1874, p. 306.

11 E. Plon, *Leone Leoni et Pompeo Leoni,* Paris, 1887, p. 298.

12 S. de Ricci, *Exposition d'objets d'art du moyen-âge et de la renaissance tirés des collections particulières de la France et de l'étranger . . . à l'ancien Hôtel de Sagan, mai–juin, 1913,* Paris, 1914, Pl. XXX.

13 É. Bertaux, "Une Exposition d'art du moyen-âge et de la renaissance," *Revue de l'art ancien et moderne,* XXXIV, 1913, pp. 16–17.

14 P. Vitry, "Exposition d'objets d'art du moyen-âge et de la renaissance," *Les Arts,* No. 141, 1913, p. 30.

HUBERT GERHARD, Attributed to

1540/50 (?)–1620

Born probably in s'Hertogenbosch during the 1540s, Gerhard seems to have been trained in Italy in the workshop of Giovanni Bologna. He had moved to Germany by 1581 to execute the Christoph Fugger altar for the Dominican Church at Augsburg, and in this work (of which the figurative sections are now in London) the fruits of his contact with Giovanni Bologna are clearly evident. From 1583 Gerhard was employed by Hans Fugger at Kirchheim, notably on a fountain (1584–94) of which the principal group survives in the Bayerisches Nationalmuseum, Munich; concurrently he worked on a celebrated fountain at Augsburg. Before 1587 he entered the service of Duke Wilhelm V of Bavaria in Munich. Thereafter he was attached to the court of the Archduke Maximilian der Deutschmeister, dividing his time between Innsbruck and Munich. He died in Munich in 1620.

Triton and Nereid (16.2.63)

Bronze: H. 25½ in. (64.8 cm).

Description: The Triton kneels astride a large conch shell, with the upper part of his body twisted diagonally and his left shoulder advanced. He gazes upwards to his right at the Nereid, whom he clasps with both arms. The Nereid's right foot is set on one of the two curled tails of the Triton, her left knee is bent, and her lower left leg rests on his hip. Her head is turned frontally. She covers her left breast with her right hand, and rests her left hand on the Triton's back. The irregular rounded base with conventionalized waves is cast in one with the remainder of the group.

Condition: Medium brown bronze (for patination see below). There are some small casting flaws, especially at the back, where one flaw has been repaired with a bronze insert. Other inserts are in the upper right arm and the left hand and forearm of the Triton, and on the Triton's neck. The bronze is fixed with screws to a modern steel plate.

It is inferred by Maclagan[1] that the group was intended to serve as a fountain. In this event there would have been two water jets, one through the Triton's mouth, which is bored with a circular hole ⅜ in. (1 cm) in diameter, and the other in the middle of the conch, which was cast open but is fitted with an irregular almond-shaped bronze plate fixed with lead solder; the bronze of the plate ap-

pears to be contemporary with the remainder of the group, but it has in the center a hole ⅞ in. (2.2 cm) in diameter filled with a modern stud. There is no trace inside the group of any piping, and the three holes bored through the base are designed for fixing, not for water pipes. The patination on the caps of the modern studs (corks fitted with bronze caps) which fill these holes is indistinguishable from the patination of the remainder of the group and suggests that the whole group has been repatinated; remains of the original dark patination survive in the hollows and crevices at the back.

The group was ascribed to Adriaen de Vries when in the Mannheim collection (see below), and is so designated by Bode,[2] who regarded it as the top of a fountain. A related pen drawing in the Kupferstichkabinett at Munich,[3] inscribed in the upper right corner with the name of Adriaen de Vries, is noted by Buchwald[4] and published by Brinckmann[5] as a work of de Vries of about 1620, in both cases without reference to the present group. The connection between the drawing and the bronze was first established by Welcker,[6] who retains the attribution to Adriaen de Vries for both works, but demonstrates, on the basis of authenticated signatures, that the inscription on the drawing is of later date and is not in de Vries' handwriting. The bronze is accepted by Strohmer[7] with a dating about 1620, but the drawing is rejected as a copy on account of its incompatibility with a drawing at Dresden identified by Holzhausen[8] on graphological grounds as a work of de Vries. The bronze and the drawing are both accepted as early works of de Vries by Weihrauch,[9] but are excised from the de Vries catalogue by Larsson,[10] who dismisses them as the work of an unidentified sculptor.

The drawing at Munich (pen and brown ink heightened in white; watermark of a crowned lion in a shield related to but not identical with Briquet 10593) has no more than a generic resemblance to the drawings of de Vries. Differences in the poses of the two figures and in the form of the shell suggest that it is, nonetheless, a study for and not a copy from the bronze. The closest point of reference for the present group in the work of Adriaen de Vries is the *Virtue Overcoming Vice* in the National Gallery of Art, Washington (Widener Collection), which is signed and dated 1610, but there are marked technical discrepancies between the two works: the Washington bronze lacks the chiselling which is so prominent a feature of the present group, the pupils of the eyes are treated differently, and the modelling, especially of the hair, is softer and more fluent. Comparison of the

two bronzes seems to prove conclusively that one artist cannot have been responsible for both. The technical peculiarities which preclude an attribution to de Vries recur in a number of other bronzes, of which the most important is the *Mars, Venus, and Amor* in Vienna.[11] This group was at one time ascribed to de Vries, but is now accepted as a late work by Hubert Gerhard; it makes use of the motif of the central group from the Kirchheim fountain (1584–94) in the Bayerisches Nationalmuseum, Munich.[12]

Attention is drawn by Bode[13] to the use in the present group of motifs derived from Giovanni Bologna, whose *Florence Triumphant Over Pisa* is cited as its source. A more specific derivation can be traced in the pose of the Triton, which depends from the standing male figure in the *Rape of the Sabines,* and the completion of the full-scale model for that work (marble finished 1582), with which Gerhard must have become familiar in Italy in or prior to 1581, provides a *terminus post quem* for the present statuette. The Frick group is perhaps contemporary with the Kirchheim fountain, and is considerably earlier than the Vienna bronze, which is regarded by Weihrauch as a product of the sculptor's last years at Innsbruck.

Exhibited: New York, Metropolitan Museum, 1914–16, No. 165, lent by the J. Pierpont Morgan Estate.

Collections: Charles Mannheim, Paris. Sold by him, in May 1901, to J. Pierpont Morgan, London and New York.[14] Duveen. Frick, 1916.

NOTES

1 E. Maclagan, in *The Frick Collection Catalogue,* VI, 1954, pp. 21–22.

2 W. Bode, *Collection of J. Pierpont Morgan: Bronzes of the Renaissance and Subsequent Periods,* Paris, 1910, I, p. xxxiv, II, p. 17, No. 165, Pl. CXIV.

3 15⅛ × 10 in. (38.5 × 25.5 cm).

4 C. Buchwald, *Adriaen de Vries,* Leipzig, 1899, pp. 31–32.

5 A. E. Brinckmann, *Barockskulptur,* Berlin–Neubabelsberg, 1919, I, p. 170, Fig. 166; *Süddeutsche Bronzebildhauer des Frühbarocks,* Munich, 1923, p. 37, Fig. 88.

6 A. Welcker, "Adrianus de Vries Hagiensis Pictor et Statuarius," *Oud Holland,* LV, 1938, pp. 193–200.

7 E. V. Strohmer, "Bemerkungen zu den Werken des Adriaen de Vries," *Nationalmusei Årsbok 1947–1948,* Stockholm, 1950, pp. 110, 138.

8 W. Holzhausen, "Eine Zeichnung des Adriaen de Vries im Staatlichen Kupferstichkabinett zu Dresden," *Die graphischen Künste,* N.F. V, 1940, pp. 72–74.

9 H. R. Weihrauch, *Europäische Bronzestatuetten,* Brunswick, 1967, pp. 350, 353.

10 L. O. Larsson, *Adrian de Vries,* Vienna–Munich, 1967, p. 127.

11 L. Planiscig, *Die Bronzeplastiken,* 1924, pp. 201–03, No. 326.

12 See H. R. Weihrauch, *Bayerisches National-museum: Die Bildwerke in Bronze und in an-deren Metallen,* Munich, 1956, pp. 137–40, No. 171, for an exemplary analysis.

13 *Loc. cit.*

14 Sold separately from the rest of the Mann-heim collection, and not in the Mannheim catalogue.

ADRIAEN DE VRIES, Attributed to

c. 1560–1626

Adriaen de Vries was born about 1560 at The Hague. Trained in the Florentine workshop of Giovanni Bologna, he appears to have worked on the complex of bronze sculptures executed by this artist for the Grimaldi Chapel in S. Francesco di Castelletto, Genoa, between 1579 and 1585. In 1588, after a stay in Rome, he entered the service of Charles Emanuel I, Duke of Savoy, and beginning in 1593 he was engaged on works for the Emperor Rudolph II, the first of which is a large group of Mercury Conducting Psyche to Olympus *now in the Louvre. De Vries worked at the imperial court in Prague from 1601 till the death of the Emperor in 1612; his development in these years is marked by a large number of signed and dated works. The principal works of de Vries' concluding phase are nine large bronze statues commissioned by King Christian IV of Denmark for a fountain for Schloss Frederiksborg, now at Drottningholm (1623), and a group of bronzes executed for the Waldstein Palace in Prague, now also at Drottningholm (1623–27). De Vries died in Prague in 1626.*

Nessus and Deianira (15.2.49)

Bronze: H. 34¾ in. (88.3 cm).

Description: The centaur Nessus gallops forward, with front hooves off the ground. His head and the upper part of his body are inclined to his right. He holds the struggling Deianira with his right arm, which is swung across his chest, and with his left hand, which grasps her right shoulder. Deianira is seated on the centaur's back with her right knee drawn up and her left leg outstretched. With her right hand she holds her cloak, which has fallen onto the centaur's back, and her left arm is raised vertically in a gesture of appeal. There is no base.

Condition: Medium brown bronze patinated golden brown. There is a flaw or join through the base of the centaur's tail, which may have been cast separately. The end of Deianira's cloak and the middle finger of her left hand have been broken and repaired. A small rectangular section has been excised from the centaur's rear right leg and strengthened with lead to rectify the thinness of the cast.

Two groups of *Nessus and Deianira* depending from models by Giovanni Bologna are known.[1] In one, the smaller model, the figure of Deianira is held to

40

the right of the body of Nessus and the centaur's head is inclined to his left, while in the other, the larger model, the figures are posed as in the present bronze. The first of these groups is probably identical with "Il Centauro che rapisce Deianira" which is listed by Baldinucci among the small bronzes produced from Giovanni Bologna's models. Three of the most notable of the surviving examples of this bronze are in the Grünes Gewölbe, Dresden (datable before 1587);[2] the Louvre (signed: IOA BOLOGNIE);[3] and the Huntington Art Gallery, San Marino, California (signed: IOANES BOLOGNA).[4]

The second group is sometimes thought to be identical with a *Rape of Deianira,* also described by Baldinucci, of which the cast failed and the model was preserved in the sculptor's studio till his death. This group is known through five versions, none of which is autograph. These are at Dresden;[5] in the Bode-Museum, Berlin;[6] in the Wallace Collection, London;[7] in the Hermitage, Leningrad; and the present example. Though the composition in four of these five bronzes is generally uniform, there are marked differences among them, affecting in particular the form of the folds of the drapery on the centaur's back; in the Dresden bronze these are typical of Giovanni Bologna, while in the versions in Berlin, Leningrad, and London, they are much elaborated. It may be inferred from this that the latter three bronzes are late seventeenth or eighteenth century variants of the model recorded in the bronze at Dresden. The present bronze differs from the other four versions not only in such details as the centaur's tail and the drapery folds, but in its design, in that the rear legs of the centaur are more erect; the balance and character of the group is thereby modified.

It is clear that we have here to do with a Northern variant of Giovanni Bologna's group. While in the hands of Duveen the group was ascribed to Adriaen de Vries, and it is related to Adriaen de Vries by Levi D'Ancona,[8] though with the proviso that "there are details which prevent us from attributing the group to the master himself." The bronze is of notably high quality, and the attribution to de Vries is likely to be correct. Analogies for the figure of Deianira occur in the *Nymph and Faun* at Dresden[9] and for the modelling of the lower part of the centaur in the signed *Pacing Horse* in the Castle Museum, Prague.[10] The present model was certainly known to de Vries, since the figure of Deianira recurs in the *Hercules, Nessus, and Deianira* at Drottningholm.[11] A suggestion of Levi D'Ancona[12] that, like the Drottningholm group, the large statuettes of the *Rape of Deianira* formed

42

part of a three-figure unit with a standing figure of Hercules, is unconvincing. The group at Drottningholm is dated 1622, and it is concluded by Levi D'Ancona[13] that "our group must certainly be dated after this, but it could not be much after the death of Adriaen de Vries (1626) because of its close similarities to the style and technique of the master." The probability is that the bronze, with its close reference to the practice of the Giovanni Bologna workshop, dates from a considerably earlier time.

Collections: Private collection, Paris (1914).[14] Duveen. Frick, 1915.

NOTES

1 The available information on these groups is assembled by E. Dhanens, *Jean Boulogne: Giovanni Bologna Fiammingo,* Brussels, 1956, pp. 200–03.

2 H. 16⅝ in. (42.2 cm).

3 H. 16⅛ in. (41 cm).

4 H. 16⅜ in. (41.5 cm).

5 H. 30⅛ in. (76.5 cm). See W. Holzhausen, "Die Bronzen der Kurfürstlich Sächsischen Kunstkammer zu Dresden," *Jahrbuch der Preuszischen Kunstsammlungen,* LIV, 1933, Beiheft, pp. 63–65.

6 H. 31⅞ in. (81 cm). See W. von Bode and E. F. Bange, *Bildwerke des Kaiser-Friedrich-Museums: Bronzestatuetten,* Berlin-Leipzig, 1930, p. 35, No. 165.

7 H. 32¼ in. (81.9 cm). See J. G. Mann, *Wallace Collection Catalogues: Sculpture,* 1931, pp. 43–44, No. S 114, Pl. 36.

8 M. Levi D'Ancona, in *The Frick Collection Catalogue,* VI, 1954, pp. 23–24.

9 See L. O. Larsson, *Adrian de Vries,* Vienna–Munich, 1967, p. 119, Fig. 7.

10 *Idem,* p. 122, Fig. 106.

11 See E. V. Strohmer, "Bemerkungen zu den Werken des Adriaen de Vries," *Nationalmusei Årsbok 1947–1948,* Stockholm, 1950, pp. 112–13.

12 *Loc. cit.*

13 *Idem.*

14 Perhaps identical with a bronze sold anonymously May 11, 1914, Hôtel Drouot, Paris, Lot 77: "Groupe en bronze: l'Enlèvement de Déjanire. Socle et contresocle en marbres de couleur moulurés de bronze." See *The Frick Collection Catalogue,* VI, pp. 24–25.

NETHERLANDISH

Seventeenth Century

Venus (16.2.62)

Bronze: H. 14 in. (35.6 cm).

Description: The figure, which is cast in one with a shallow circular base with the upper surface treated naturalistically, is represented nude, gazing upwards to her left. On the crown of her head is a jewel bound by a fillet. Her weight rests on the right foot, which is placed before the left, and her right hand is extended laterally and downwards, with open palm. In her closed left hand, which is held forwards of the body, is an indecipherable object, perhaps a mirror handle.

Condition: Traces of black lacquer over light brown bronze. The ends of rusty iron nails are embedded in both hips.

The subject of the bronze is described in the Falcke sale catalogue (see below) as *Eve,* and by Maclagan,[1] probably correctly, as *Venus.* The ascription in the Falcke sale to the School of Peter Vischer is likewise dismissed by Maclagan, for whom the bronze "appears to date from the late sixteenth, or perhaps more probably from the early seventeenth century, and to be the work of an artist more probably Flemish than German."

There are no closely related German bronzes. The open pose recalls that of a female figure identified as *Fama* in Berlin (Inv. No. 1780), wrongly given by Planiscig[2] to Paolo Savin, and of a *Venus* in the Huntington Art Gallery, San Marino, California, given by Bode[3] tentatively to Francavilla and described by Wark[4] as Franco-Flemish, first half of the seventeenth century. The present figure is not by the same sculptor as these bronzes, but is likely to have been produced in their proximity.

Exhibited: New York, Metropolitan Museum, Morgan Collection, 1914–16, No. 1609, lent by the J. Pierpont Morgan Estate.

Collections: Isaac Falcke, London. His sale, April 19–22, 1910, Christie's, Lot 22, sold for 3,000 guineas to C. Davis. Arthur Sambon. Sold by him in Florence in 1912 for £600 to J. Pierpont Morgan, London and New York. Duveen. Frick, 1916.

NOTES

1 E. Maclagan, in *The Frick Collection Catalogue,* VI, 1954, pp. 30–31.

2 L. Planiscig, *Piccoli bronzi italiani del rinascimento,* Milan, 1930, Pl. CXXVII, Fig. 222.

3 W. Bode, *Collection of J. Pierpont Morgan: Bronzes of the Renaissance and Subsequent Periods,* Paris, 1910, II, No. 219, Pl. CLVI.

4 R. R. Wark, *Sculpture in the Huntington Collection,* Los Angeles, 1959, Fig. XXIII, p. 69.

JEAN BARBET

Active 1475–d. 1514

Nothing is known of Barbet before March 28, 1475, when he signed and dated the bronze figure of an Angel described below. In the same inscription he styles himself "dit de lion," and all documentary records of him relate to his activity as a founder of cannon and supplier of ordnance materials at Lyon. There is no evidence of his activity at Lyon before 1491, when he assumed the title of Canonnier du Roy, *but from that year until 1507 he was employed, together with his brother Valentin, by the Consulat of Lyon as* canonnier et bombardier, *charged with the maintenance of the city's artillery and with casting cannon and cannonballs. In 1503 taxes due from him to the Crown were suspended by the Consulat "a cause qu'il est canonnier et a servy la ville et est pour la servir." Barbet is recorded in 1513 as receiving payment from the city of Lyon for a consignment of gunpowder. He died at Lyon the following year.*

Angel (43.2.82)

Inscribed, in Gothic characters running vertically on the inside of the left wing: *le xxvii^i jour de mars | lan mil cccc lx + xv jehan barbet dit de lion fist cest angelot.* Bronze: H. with wings 46^{11}/16 in. (118.6 cm); H. of figure 45^{11}/16 in. (116.1 cm).

Description: The figure wears an alb gathered in at the waist and falling in deep folds to his feet; its wide collar is turned back at the neck. His right hand is held forward of the body, with the thumb raised and the first finger extended in a pointing gesture. The left hand, also held before the body, is clenched, and seems originally to have held some object, probably a staff or cross, measuring ⅞ in. (2.2 cm) in diameter. The head is bent slightly forwards, and the long hair is brushed up at the sides over a wide band decorated above the forehead with a rosette; the hair on top of the head, within the band,

is heavily and irregularly chiselled, and is less finely worked than that beneath. The two wings, which extend from a point 1 in. (2.5 cm) above the head to approximately calf level, are each fixed with three bronze pins (apparently original) to sockets attached to the shoulder blades. The bare feet of the figure rest on a small irregular mound. There is evidence of extensive chiselling on the fingernails and toenails, the hair, wings, and eyes, and the rosette above the forehead.

Condition: Dark brown patina over a light brown copper alloy. The figure is pitted with small flaws, especially on the chin, and several larger flaws have been filled with brown tinted wax. The tips of two feathers of the right wing and one feather of the left wing have been broken off. The ends of three rusty iron bars are visible at each side of the figure: one, measuring 1⅜ × ⅜ in. (3.5 × 1 cm), occurs at waist height; another, measuring 1 × ⅜ in. (2.5 × 1 cm), is on the level of the knees; and the third, of the same dimensions, appears 5¹¹/₁₆ in. (14.5 cm) from the bottom of the figure. In each case the ends of the bars are carefully shaped in with the drapery. On the top of the head is an irregular rectangular hole, approximately 1 × 1³/₁₆ in. (2.5 × 3 cm), filled with an unchased bronze plug of lighter metal, seemingly a later filling. The figure is reported to have been exposed in the open air at Lude (see below) and may originally have been intended for such a position. In these circumstances the present patina would be inexplicable, and it is concluded by Biebel[1] that it is "probably of recent origin. In a test cleaning on a small section of one of the wing lugs, an area normally hidden from view, the removal of the brown patina disclosed a surface color of light yellow. Whether the original surface color was intended to be light yellow is still uncertain, but if so, the transformation the figure would undergo by the removal of the patina can be imagined, changing it from a figure of rather somber tone to one of bright and shining appearance."

The provenance of the *Angel* presents problems of some difficulty. A letter of May 7, 1921 (now in the Pierpont Morgan Library), from A. E. Merriman Paff of Paris to Belle da Costa Greene, transcribes the following information, stated to have been obtained from M. d'Hendecourt: "Please tell Miss Greene in confidence that the Ange du Lude was found by Du Sommerard among the cast-outs of the Sainte Chapelle at the time of its restoration. It was one of the four girouettes; another one was supposed to have been found at the same time but has disappeared. Du Sommerard bought it off the architect, who was a personal friend of his, and sold it in great mystery to his cousin the Marquis de Talhouet, pledging him not to give away the provenance as the Angel would otherwise have been claimed by the French Government." If this information is correct, the *Angel* would have been acquired by Alexandre du Sommerard (1779–1842), Director of

the Musée de Cluny, about 1840. The *Angel* was subsequently owned by the Marquis de Talhouet, Château du Lude, Sarthe, where it is said to have been used initially as a *girouette* or weather vane on one of the towers of the château, and where it later stood on the newel post of an interior staircase.[2]

An alternative provenance is contained in a letter of March 14, 1951, from Paul Mallon to the Director of The Frick Collection, stating that the *Angel* reached the Château du Lude from the Cathedral at nearby Le Mans: "J'habite en France, le château de la Jaille, à 25 kilometres du château du Lude, que je connais fort bien. Je me suis toujours occupé d'archéologie et de l'art de ma province du Maine.... Au Mans dans mes recherches, j'ai lu dans des annales du pays, dans une revue, que cet ange était celui de la Cathédrale du Mans, qu'il avait été jeté bas à la Révolution. Ramassé par un des membres de la famille Talhouet il était venu échouer au château du Lude où il était resté, non à cause de sa beauté, mais en souvenir des journées révolutionnaires." Efforts to locate the review in question have been unsuccessful, and there is no supporting evidence for this statement.

The *Angel* was exhibited at the Paris Exposition Universelle in 1867 by the Marquis de Talhouet.[3] It was bought from him by Félix Wildenstein, probably in 1905, and passed from Wildenstein to Georges Hoentschel of Paris, by whom a cast was presented to the Trocadéro (now the Palais de Chaillot).[4] The *Angel* then passed from the Hoentschel collection to that of J. Pierpont Morgan.[5] The bill of sale of April 26, 1906 (preserved in the Pierpont Morgan Library), reads as follows: "Une statuette de bronze représentant un Angelo *[sic]* provenant du Château de Lude appartenant au Marquis de Talhouet lequel le tenait de Monsieur du Sommerard ancien Directeur du Musée du Cluny comme étant girouette de la Sainte-Chapelle." The purchase price, which also included two minor objects, was £40,000. After the death of Pierpont Morgan, the *Angel* was shown in the Pierpont Morgan Library (whence it was lent in 1940 to the Boston Museum of Fine Arts[6]) until 1943, when it was sold through Knoedler to The Frick Collection.

In the literature of French sculpture, three main theories have been advanced as to the original destination of the figure. The first of these, that the *Angel* was made for the Château du Lude, is supported by Vitry,[7] who suggests that it was commissioned by Jean Daillon, seigneur of Lude, by Bode,[8] Aubert,[9] and Evans,[10] and by Müller,[11] who describes it as "the bronze figure from the top of the tower of the Château du Lude, representing an angel which, according to the inscription

52

on one of the wings, was made by 'Jehan Barbet dit de Lion' in 1475 for Jean Daillon, lord of the said castle." The claim that the *Angel* was made for the Château du Lude is in conflict with the evidence cited above. The second theory is that the *Angel* was brought to Lude from Saint-Martin d'Ablois (Marne). This case, which is unsubstantiated, is stated by Palustre.[12] The third theory, that the *Angel* was acquired in Paris and moved thence to the Château du Lude, is accepted by Enlart and Roussel.[13] Though Biebel[14] concludes that "until further documentation makes it possible to determine the exact source, it is best to describe the angel as coming from an unknown location," the evidence that it was acquired in Paris, possibly from the Sainte-Chapelle, is stronger than that for any other provenance.

The Sainte-Chapelle was built between 1243 and 1248. There is no record of its external appearance at the time of its completion, but in 1383, under Charles VI, a new *flèche* was built, and the church is represented in this form in the *Très Riches Heures*. In 1460 the roof was renewed and a third *flèche* was constructed. The form of the roof and *flèche* are recorded in 1583 in a drawing by Jacques Cellier, now in the Bibliothèque Nationale.[15] This roof and *flèche* were destroyed by fire in 1630. Though the Cellier drawing shows no angel on the roof, a drawing by Chastillon, engraved by Brébiette and published in 1641,[16] but made prior to 1630,[17] does show an angel on a tall plinth on the *chevet,* as well as a series of music-making angels placed on the gables above each window in front of the balustrade. As observed by Gébelin,[18] the angels on the balustrade appear to date from the late sixteenth or early seventeenth century. The angel on the *chevet* cannot be identical with the Barbet *Angel,* since its dimensions are incompatible, it is dressed in flowing drapery, and it holds a circlet, presumably the Crown of Thorns, in its right hand. An engraving by Ransonnette, cited by Biebel as showing the Sainte-Chapelle before the fire of 1630, is a fanciful late eighteenth century reconstruction based on the Brébiette engraving and incorporating other features from late seventeenth century engravings with some imaginary elements; this engraving forms the frontispiece to S.-J. Morand's *Histoire de la Sainte Chapelle Royale du Palais,* published in Paris in 1790.

The fire of 1630 completely destroyed the roof of the Sainte-Chapelle. Rebuilding was ordered in 1634 and completed in 1671. A drawing by Martellange in the Cabinet des Estampes of the Bibliothèque Nationale[19] shows the building with no

roof. The new roof and *flèche* are recorded in late seventeenth century engravings by Silvestre and Boisseau and in a late eighteenth century engraving by Ransonnette,[20] but in none of these is there evidence of the presence of an angel or *girouette*. The sacristy of the Sainte-Chapelle, in somewhat the same form as the church, to whose north side it was attached, was demolished following a fire in the Cour de Mai in 1776. A late seventeenth century engraving by Boisseau[21] shows that it had a *chevet* of similar shape to that of the main building, but it appears not to have been surmounted by an angel.

The Sainte-Chapelle was condemned for demolition in 1790, but was reprieved. In 1793 it was mutilated by the removal of the royal insignia and the *flèche,* but some of the interior fittings, including four statues of Apostles from the upper chapel, were saved by Lenoir. In 1836 a plan for its restoration was presented by Lassus, and in 1840 work began under Duban. Duban was succeeded in 1849 by Lassus, who died in 1857 having completed the exterior, including the provision of a new angel for the *chevet.*[22] It is wrongly claimed by Biebel[23] that the angel by Lassus was copied from that shown in the Brébiette engraving; not only is it unrelated to that in the engraving, but it is known to have been inspired by Lassus' study of Villard de Honnecourt and to have been executed to his design by the sculptor Dechaume.[24]

So far as concerns the alleged provenance of the Frick *Angel* from the Sainte-Chapelle it must, therefore, be concluded *(i)* that this is not corroborated by any of the sources for the external appearance of the church in or after the sixteenth century, but *(ii)* that it could well have been retrieved from the church at the time of the Lassus restoration. Since the inscription on the left wing of the *Angel* testifying that it was completed on March 28, 1475, is expressed in the highly unusual form *"mil cccc lx + xv,"* it is possible that this refers to the completion of the *Angel* fifteen years after the construction (in 1460) of the new roof and *flèche* of which it was intended to form part.

The inscription also records that the *Angel* was cast by Jean Barbet of Lyon.[25] Barbet is recorded as active at Lyon,[26] where he was employed as a founder of cannon. He became *Canonnier du Roy* in 1491, and till 1507 was employed with his brother, Valentin, by the Consulat of Lyon as *canonnier et bombardier.*[27] As concluded by Biebel, it is likely that Barbet was the caster, not the designer, of the figure.

56

The use in the inscription of the term *angelot* as a diminutive of *ange* is analyzed by Biebel,[28] who plausibly suggests that "the most reasonable explanation is that the angel ... was designed on the scale of a monumental, life-size figure but [that] compared to a height of six feet, its height of less than four feet is diminutive." If this explanation is accepted, it affords a supporting argument for the view that the *Angel* was designed for external, not internal, use.

The information obtained from D'Hendecourt cited in the letter printed above states that the *Angel* was one of four *girouettes* from the Sainte-Chapelle, and in the catalogue of the Exposition Universelle of 1867[29] it is said to have been installed at Lude probably "en guise de girouette." The theory that the *Angel* was designed as a weather vane is accepted by Bode,[30] Vitry,[31] and Roussel,[32] but is questioned by Biebel,[33] principally on the ground that the form of the wings is not consistent with this function and that the *Angel,* given its heavy weight, would not have turned easily. Nevertheless, the exceptionally strong and complex iron structure inside the figure constitutes in itself an argument that the *Angel* was designed to fulfill this or some similar function. At least one case[34] is, however, known of an angel holding a weather vane in its left hand; this occurs at Le Dorat (Haute-Vienne).[35] The possibility is raised by Biebel[36] that the *Angel* was instead a "turning angel," which worked on a clock principle with weights turning a central screw; such a mechanism "par chu fait om un ange tenir son doit ades vers le solel" is described by Villard de Honnecourt. Despite statements to the contrary, there is no evidence that the lost angel on the east end of the Sainte-Chapelle was of this type. Though it has been claimed[37] that the Barbet *Angel* was originally made for the position later occupied by the angel of Lassus, the discrepancy in the dimensions and the great height at which it would have been exhibited are rightly held by Biebel to preclude this possibility.

Alternatively it has been suggested that the figure was made for internal use. According to Palustre,[38] it would have been one of four angels on columns frequently used for marking off the enclosure of the high altar. Four such angels, of "fin cuyvre dore," are mentioned in an inventory of Saint-Denis of 1505,[39] and one of these is reproduced in a painting of *The Mass of St. Giles* in the National Gallery, London. A second hypothesis, also advanced by Palustre,[40] is that the present figure formed one of a group of angels with the Instruments of the Passion. A further theory is put forward by Biebel[41] that the bronze may have served as an

annunciatory angel from an Annunciation group. The statement of D'Hendecourt that the *Angel* was originally one of four figures, of which a second was allegedly discovered in the first half of the nineteenth century, would, if true, preclude this possibility. The strongly fortified interior of the figure lends no support to the theory that it was originally intended for internal use.

Exhibited: Paris, Exposition Universelle, Histoire du travail, 1867, No. 1827, lent by the Marquis de Talhouet. Boston Museum of Fine Arts, Arts of the Middle Ages: 1000–1400, 1940, No. 199.

Collections: Marquis de Talhouet, Château du Lude, Sarthe. Félix Wildenstein. Georges Hoentschel, Paris. J. Pierpont Morgan, London and New York, 1906. Knoedler. Frick, 1943.

NOTES

1 F. M. Biebel, "The 'Angelot' of Jean Barbet," *Art Bulletin,* XXXII, 1950, p. 338.

2 A photograph of the staircase with the *Angel* in place is reproduced by Biebel, *op. cit.,* Fig. 7.

3 *Catalogue Histoire du travail,* Paris, 1867, p. 115, No. 1827. See also: C. de Linas, *L'Histoire du travail à l'Exposition Universelle de 1867,* Paris, 1867, p. 286; C. de Linas, "L'Histoire du travail à l'Exposition Universelle de 1867," *Revue de l'art chrétien,* 1ʳᵉ sér., XI, 1867, p. 640; A. Darcel, "Le Bronze dans les salles de l'Histoire du travail," *Gazette des Beaux-Arts,* 1ʳᵉ pér., XXIII, 1867, p. 316.

4 See Georges Hoentschel sale catalogue, Galerie Georges Petit, Paris, March 31–April 2, 1919, p. xi.

5 W. Bode, *Collection of J. Pierpont Morgan: Bronzes of the Renaissance and Subsequent Periods,* Paris, 1910, I, pp. xli, 1–2, No. 2, Pls. I–III.

6 *Arts of the Middle Ages: 1000–1400,* Boston Museum of Fine Arts, 1940, p. 60, No. 199.

7 P. Vitry, *Michel Colombe et la sculpture française de son temps,* Paris, 1901, pp. 84–86.

8 *Loc. cit.*

9 M. Aubert, *La Sculpture française au moyen-âge,* Paris, 1946, p. 410.

10 J. Evans, *Art in Medieval France,* London, 1948, p. 172.

11 C. T. Müller, *Sculpture in the Netherlands, Germany, France and Spain: 1400–1500,* London, 1966, p. 137.

12 L. Palustre, "Un Bronze du XVᵉ siècle," *Bulletin monumental,* Tours, 1878, XLIV, pp. 165–66; "Un Bronze du XVᵉ siècle," *Recueil mensuel de l'union-historique et littéraire du Maine,* Le Mans, 1895, I, pp. 231–34.

13 C. Enlart and J. Roussel, *Catalogue général du Musée de Sculpture comparée: Palais du Trocadéro,* Paris, 1910, p. 144, No. E. 89. J. Roussel, *La Sculpture française, IV: Époque gothique,* III, Paris, 1932, p. 15.

14 *Op. cit.,* p. 339.

15 See H. Stein, *Le Palais de Justice et la Sainte-Chapelle de Paris,* Paris, 1912, facing p. 109.

16 In *Topographie française,* Paris, 1641.

17 See F. Gébelin, *La Sainte-Chapelle et la Conciergerie,* Paris, 1931, p. 11.

18 *Idem,* p. 22.

19 See Stein, *op. cit.,* facing p. 120.

20 See Morand, *op. cit.,* facing p. 37.

21 See L. Grodecki, *Sainte-Chapelle,* Paris, 1963, p. 15.

22 For the work undertaken at this time, see: M. de Guilhermy, *La Sainte-Chapelle de Paris après ses restaurations,* Paris, 1857; J.-B.-A. Lassus, "La Sainte-Chapelle du Palais," in H. Carpentier, *Paris dans sa splendeur,* Paris, 1861.

23 *Op. cit.,* p. 341.

24 Guilhermy, *op. cit.,* p. 2.

25 For the epigraphy of the inscription and the date, see Biebel, *op. cit.,* p. 337.

26 N. Rondot, *L'Art et les artistes à Lyon du XIVe au XVIIIe siècle,* Lyon, 1902, p. 17.

27 M. Audin and E. Vial, *Dictionnaire des artistes et ouvriers d'art du Lyonnais,* I, Paris, 1918, p. 52.

28 *Op. cit.,* pp. 337–38.

29 *Catalogue Histoire du travail, loc. cit.*

30 *Loc. cit.*

31 *Loc. cit.*

32 *Loc. cit.*

33 *Op. cit.,* p. 340.

34 Cited by Biebel, *op. cit.,* p. 341.

35 For this see A. de Laborderie, "Églises et vieilles maisons du Dorat," *Bulletin de la Société archéologique et historique du Limousin,* LXXVII, 1938, p. 399.

36 *Op. cit.,* pp. 340–41.

37 *Arts of the Middle Ages, loc. cit.; Art News,* XLIII, February 15, 1944, p. 8, caption to photograph.

38 *Loc. cit.*

39 See Biebel, *op. cit.,* pp. 342–43.

40 *Loc. cit.*

41 *Op. cit.,* pp. 343–44.

FRENCH

Middle of the Seventeenth Century

Hercules and the Hydra (15.2.53)

Bronze: H. 22⅜ in. (56.8 cm).

Description: Hercules is posed diagonally on an irregular rectangular naturalistic base. His legs straddle the body of the seven-headed Hydra, which crouches beneath him on a reverse diagonal. Hercules bends to his left and grips one of the monster's necks with his left hand, while swinging his club over his head to strike at the rearing heads to his right. One beaked mouth bites at his right hip, and another at his right ankle. His right foot presses down on the clawed left hind foot of the monster. Its clawed left foreleg protrudes across the rear left corner of the base.

Condition: Dark brown lacquer (much rubbed) over medium yellowish-brown bronze. Maclagan's comment[1] that "there are carefully executed repairs on the bronze, which suggest a fault in casting round the waist," is incorrect. There are twenty-two joins throughout the group, and of these only two appear to result from breaks. All the protruding elements are cast separately and have been pinned or brazed together with great skill.

When exhibited in 1874 and in 1908 (see below), the group was ascribed to Giovanni Bologna. It is assumed by Maclagan[2] that the model "is derived from Giovanni Bologna," though "due to one of his later followers." The disposition of the group is related to a wax model in the Palazzo Vecchio, Florence,[3] where the figure of Hercules is also set diagonally across a rectangular base, his right arm and club are raised, and his left hand grips the tail of the Hydra, which again is set on a reverse diagonal. This model is tentatively connected by Dhanens[4] with a silver group of *Hercules and the Hydra* from a model by Giovanni Bologna to which reference is made in a document of 1580/81. Though the stance and type of Hercules in the wax model differ somewhat and the treatment of the Hydra differs totally from those in the present group, there can be little doubt that the bronze depends, directly or obliquely, from the wax model. An inventory of March 20, 1684, of the collection of Louis XIV of France[5] lists as Nos. 34 and 50 "un Hercules frapant sur l'hydre qu'il tient par la queue' an" and "un Hercules qui assomme un dragon qu'il arreste par le col, de main gauche." The first of these

62

entries seems to refer to a bronze based on the wax model, of which a version is reproduced by Bode,[6] and the second to a bronze of which a version exists in the Museo degli Argenti of the Palazzo Pitti, Florence. There is thus no difficulty in supposing that the present group derives from the wax model through one or more bronze statuettes.

When the present group was exhibited in Paris in 1874, it was argued by Mantz[7] that though in the style of Giovanni Bologna "elle pourrait aussi bien être de Francheville ou de son gendre Bordone. C'est, pour nous, une oeuvre franco-italienne." It was also claimed by Mantz that the head of Hercules, which is strikingly dissimilar from that in the prototypes by or after Giovanni Bologna, reproduced the features of Henry IV of France, and that the group was planned as an allegory of the struggle of Henry IV against the League. These claims are accepted by Bode,[8] who ascribes the bronze to the French School of the beginning of the seventeenth century. The identification as Henry IV is rejected by Maclagan,[9] but is accepted by the editors of *The Frick Collection Catalogue*.[10] Comparison with the portraits of Henry IV suggests that the identification is likely to be correct. The comparison of Henry IV with Hercules[11] originates in the belief, already current in the sixteenth century, that Hercules was the progenitor of the house of Navarre. According to Valladier,[12] Hercules, having recovered the herds stolen by Geryon in Spain, and slain the Lominians, the children of Geryon, thus freeing the people of Spain from servitude, set up his son Hispalus as King of Spain. The latter's descendants later succeeded to the crown of Navarre, and were thus the ancestors of Henry IV. In Ronsard's *Franciade* the classical hero is assimilated to the traditional French figure of the Gallic Hercules, a mythical personage also identified with the god Olmius, the protector of the Gauls, who was possessed not only of great courage and physical prowess, but of a peculiar gift of conquest by persuasive speech. The Gallic Hercules was portrayed in the sixteenth century in a form identical to that of the classical Hercules, and had a special appeal to Henry IV, whose aim was to defend, pacify, and unify France as much by negotiation as by force of arms. Henry IV is first portrayed as Hercules during the civil war in a medal of 1592, which depicts him subduing Cerberus. In a volume published in the preceding year[13] this subject and that of Hercules subduing the Hydra are stated to signify "Imperatorem vel Principem clara virtute sua domare et excutere vitia a suis populis cum iustis et sanctis legibus." Vivanti[14] reproduces two engravings show-

64

ing Henry IV as Hercules subduing the Hydra; the first reproduces a group set up at Henry's ceremonial entry into Lyon in 1595, and the second reproduces one of the nine triumphal arches set up for the entry of Marie de Médicis into Avignon in 1600, each of which was surmounted by a scene from the legend of Hercules, portrayed with the features of the King, that of Hercules and the Hydra symbolizing Henry IV's victories against the League. The King is also represented as triumphant over the Hydra in an engraving by Léonard Gautier[15] and elsewhere.

It is further argued by the editors of *The Frick Collection Catalogue*[16] that if the bronze is French and dates from the early seventeenth century "we are left with the two names suggested by Mantz as the only possible authors," and that since the bronze is demonstrably not by Francavilla, it must therefore be by Bordoni (c. 1580–1656), who was responsible in 1618 for finishing the four bronze slaves modelled by Francavilla for the base of the equestrian monument of Henry IV on the Pont Neuf, Paris. The slaves are not so closely related to the present bronze as to make an attribution to Bordoni mandatory. Moreover, though the group depends from a composition by Giovanni Bologna, its technique is altogether unlike that used in the Bologna workshop, and might in itself constitute an argument against ascribing it to a direct pupil of Giovanni Bologna. In practice the bronze can be attributed only to a studio in which sectional casting was employed as generally and skillfully as it is here, and it may have been produced as late as the third quarter of the seventeenth century. It has been observed by Landais[17] that a gilt bronze group of a warrior in combat with a dragon (Louvre), formerly at Versailles and apparently of late seventeenth century date, is cast sectionally in a manner analogous to the present bronze.[18]

Exhibited: Paris, Palais du Corps législatif, Exposition en faveur de l'oeuvre des Alsaciens et Lorrains, April 1874, lent by Frédéric Spitzer.[19] Boston Museum of Fine Arts, Renaissance and Modern Bronzes, 1908, No. 34, lent by Duveen.

Collections: Frédéric Spitzer, Paris. Oscar Hainauer, Berlin. Duveen. Frick, 1915.

NOTES

1 E. Maclagan, in *The Frick Collection Catalogue,* VI, 1954, p. 34.

2 *Idem.*

3 Donazione Loeser, formerly collection of Bernardo Vecchietti.

4 E. Dhanens, *Jean Boulogne: Giovanni Bo-*

logna *Fiammingo,* Brussels, 1956, pp. 189–91.

5 For which see L. Courajod, report in *Bulletin de la Société nationale des antiquaires de France,* Paris, 1882, p. 220.

6 W. Bode, *The Italian Bronze Statuettes of the Renaissance,* III, London, 1912, Fig. 10.

7 P. Mantz, "Exposition en faveur de l'oeuvre des Alsaciens et Lorrains," *Gazette des Beaux-Arts,* 2ᵉ pér., X, 1874, pp. 305–06.

8 W. Bode, *Die Sammlung Oscar Hainauer,* Berlin, 1897, p. 78, No. 111.

9 *Loc. cit.*

10 VI, pp. 34–36.

11 C. Vivanti, "Henry IV, the Gallic Hercules," *Journal of the Warburg and Courtauld Institutes,* 1967, pp. 176–97.

12 *Labyrinthe Royal de l'Hercule Gaulois Triomphant, représenté à l'entrée triomphante de la Royne en la cité d'Avignon le 19 nov. de l'an MDC,* 1601, quoted by J. Seznec in *La Survivance des dieux antiques,* London, 1940, pp. 28–29.

13 Antonio Ricciardo Brixiano, *Commentaria symbolica,* Venice, 1591, p. 33.

14 *Loc. cit.*

15 Written communication of Jacques de Laprade.

16 *Loc. cit.*

17 H. Landais, personal communication, February 1969.

18 See G. Migeon, *Catalogue des bronzes et cuivres,* Paris, 1904, pp. 196–97, No. 227.

19 *Notice sommaire des objets d'art exposés au profit de la colonisation de l'Algérie par les Alsacien-Lorrains,* 2ᵉ sér., Paris, 1874, p. 30.

FRENCH AND BRITISH SCULPTURE

Eighteenth and Nineteenth Centuries

After
FRANÇOIS GIRARDON

1628–1715

Born at Troyes, the son of a maître-fondeur, *Girardon studied in Rome between 1648 and 1650. After a brief return to Troyes he settled in Paris. He was received into the Academy in 1657 and in the following year worked under Le Brun at Vaux-le-Vicomte. From 1664 onwards he was occupied mainly with official commissions, especially (after 1666) with sculpture at Versailles. Eventually a number of other artists were employed on the execution of his designs. Girardon also formed an important private art collection, which is illustrated in engravings published about 1710.*

The Grand Dauphin (15.2.64)

Executed probably in the eighteenth century after a model of about 1700. Bronze: H. 16¼ in. (41.3 cm).

Description: The Dauphin looks to his right. He wears a flowing wig, armor which is decorated on the left pauldron with intertwined dolphins, and a cravat which shows at the neck. A wide, fringed sash hangs across the breast from the right shoulder. The pupils and irises of the eyes are incised.

Condition: Dark brown lacquer (rubbed) over yellowish bronze. The casting is thin and there are some casting flaws. There is a fissure between the wig and the left cheek.

Marie-Thérèse, Queen of France (15.2.65)

Executed probably in the eighteenth century after a model of about 1700. Bronze: H. 14¼ in. (36.2 cm).

Description: The Queen looks to her right. Her hair is dressed in elaborate curls, with a long ringlet falling onto each shoulder. Over an embroidered shift and a frogged bodice she wears a fur-lined cloak embroidered with *fleurs-de-lys* and fastened by a chain. Her eyeballs are left blank.

Condition: Dark brown lacquer (rubbed) over yellowish bronze.

73

Louis, the Grand Dauphin (1661–1711), was the son of Queen Marie-Thérèse (1638–83), who had married her cousin Louis XIV in 1660. She was the daughter of Philip IV of Spain and Elizabeth of France. The Grand Dauphin, known also as Monseigneur, was the only one of her six children to survive her. He married Anne-Marie-Christine of Bavaria and by her had three sons, of whom the eldest, Louis, Duc de Bourgogne, survived him by only one year; it was thus that Louis XIV was succeeded at his death in 1715 by his great-grandson, as Louis XV. The second son of the Grand Dauphin became Philip V of Spain.

The bust of the Grand Dauphin was at one time incorrectly described as a portrait of Louis XIV by Coysevox. The true identity of both artist and subject is established by the representation of a larger version of the bust in one of the prints illustrating Girardon's private art collection:[1] in a plate entitled *Veüe d'un des Bouts de la Gallerie du Sr. Girardon Sculpteur ordinaire du Roy,* the text states that No. 1 is a "Buste de Bronze du Roy, fait par F. Girardon haut de 2. pi. 2. po.," and that No. 2 is a "Buste de Bronze de Monseigneur de pareille hauteur par le même." The bust of Monseigneur shown in the plate must therefore have measured about 26¾ in. (68 cm), or 10½ in. higher than the bronze in The Frick Collection.

The bust of Marie-Thérèse, also at one time described incorrectly as by Coysevox, is in fact a reduced copy of a posthumous portrait in marble (H. 32¹¹/₁₆ in.; 83 cm) by Girardon, formerly in the Château de Villecerf and now in the Musée de Troyes.[2] The Troyes bust is said by Guillet de Saint-Georges to have been executed by Girardon in collaboration with Martin Desjardins.[3] Also at Troyes is a companion bust of Louis XIV.

A pair of busts of the Grand Dauphin and Queen Marie-Thérèse identical to the Frick pair (save that the eyes of the Queen's portrait are not left blank) is in the Walters Art Gallery, Baltimore;[4] as in the Frick versions, the Dauphin's portrait is more thinly cast than the Queen's. A version of the Grand Dauphin is in an English private collection,[5] and a version was formerly in the collection of Edward Stotesbury, Chestnut Hill, Philadelphia.[6] Although these reduced copies, including the pair in The Frick Collection, may well date from the eighteenth century, they are of secondary quality and are unlikely to have issued from the workshop of Girardon.

Collections: Frick, 1915. (No record of the earlier history of the busts has been found.)

1 P. Francastel, *Girardon,* Paris, 1928, p. 91, No. 81, Fig. 79.

2 *Musée de Troyes: Catalogue des sculptures,* Troyes, 1882, p. 33, No. 46. See also: Francastel, *op. cit.,* p. 89, No. 74, Fig. 85; *Royal Academy, London: The Age of Louis XIV,* London, 1958, No. 66.

3 L Dussieux, E. Soulié, P. de Chennevières, P. Mantz, and A. de Montaiglon, *Mémoires inédits sur la vie et les ouvrages des membres de l'Académie royale,* Paris, 1854, I, p. 399.

4 H. R. Weihrauch, *Europäische Bronzestatuetten,* Brunswick, 1967, p. 406, Figs. 490a and b. The Baltimore versions were shipped from Seligmann & Co., Paris, to Henry Walters in 1912.

5 Sold by Gerald Kerin, Ltd., in 1967.

6 According to *The Frick Collection Catalogue,* VI, 1954, p. 37. This bust is not in the Stotesbury sale catalogues and its present location is unknown.

ANTOINE COYSEVOX

1640–1720

Born at Lyon, Coysevox went to Paris in 1657 to study with Louis Lerambert and at the Academy. He was employed at Saverne by the Bishop of Strasbourg between 1667 and 1671. After a brief return to Lyon he worked in Paris, at Versailles, and at Marly on official commissions, sepulchral monuments, and portrait busts. Coysevox was the first French sculptor to execute portraits of fellow artists and friends. Towards the end of the seventeenth century and at the beginning of the eighteenth, he dominated the field of sculpture in France. His nephews Nicolas and Guillaume Coustou, the most eminent sculptors of the next generation, were his pupils.

Robert de Cotte (45.2.83)

Executed in the early eighteenth century. Bronze: H. 21⅜ in. (54.3 cm).

Description: De Cotte looks to his right. He wears a flowing wig with curls falling over his shoulders. His neck and chest are bare, and the bust, which is severed short of the shoulder, terminates in simple drapery. Two loops for fixing are cast in one with the bust at the back.

Condition: Black lacquer over red varnish and yellowish bronze. There are several small fissures in the drapery over the left shoulder.

Robert de Cotte (1656–1735), brother-in-law and assistant to Jules-Hardouin Mansart, succeeded him as *Premier Architecte* to Louis XIV in 1708. In addition to supervising the multifarious works on French official buildings he played an important role in determining the design of a number of foreign palaces—including Buen Retiro in Madrid, Poppelsdorf, near Bonn, and the Residenz in Würzburg—by supplying drawings to the architects responsible for these buildings; he was thus the most immediately influential French architect of the early eighteenth century. He also excelled as an administrator and as an entrepreneur. De Cotte and Coysevox worked together on various projects, among them the sculpture for the choir of Notre Dame in Paris.

A marble version of the present bust, in the Bibliothèque Sainte-Geneviève, Paris, is inscribed A. COYSEVOX F. 1707;[1] a second inscription on the base records

that it was presented by de Cotte's widow in 1738. A plaster cast of the marble version, including the base, is in the Musée de Versailles.[2] A bust of Robert de Cotte by Coysevox was exhibited in the Salon of 1704;[3] the material is unspecified.

Exhibited: New York, Wildenstein, French XVIIIth Century Sculpture Formerly of the David-Weill Collection, 1940, No. 1.

Collections: Octavius E. Coope, Brentwood, Essex (?).[4] David-Weill, Paris. Wildenstein. Frick, 1945.

NOTES

1 A. Boinet, "Les Bustes de Coysevox de la Bibliothèque Sainte-Geneviève," *Gazette des Beaux-Arts,* 5ᵉ pér., II, 1920, p. 1.

2 E. Soulié, *Notice du Musée Impérial de Versailles,* I, Paris, 1859, p. 219, No. 799.

3 J.-J. Guiffrey, *Collection des livrets des anciennes expositions depuis 1673 jusqu'en 1800* (Exposition de 1704), Paris, 1869, p. 10.

4 According to G. Keller-Dorian (*Antoine Coysevox,* Paris, 1920, II, pp. 53–54, Pl. 122), the bust was included in the Octavius Coope sale, May 3–5, 1910, Christie's. No bust of de Cotte is listed in the sale catalogue, but the Frick portrait may perhaps be identified with Lot 182: "Molière; a bronze bust, life size." According to an annotated copy of the sale catalogue in The Frick Art Reference Library, Lot 182 was sold to A. Wertheimer.

ANTOINE COYSEVOX (?)

Henri de La Tour d'Auvergne, Maréchal Turenne (18.2.67)

Executed probably in the early eighteenth century. Bronze: H. 29¼ in. (74.3 cm).

Description: Turenne looks to his right. His long hair falls over the front of his right shoulder and is swept back from his left. Over a tunic he wears a cuirass decorated with foliated scrolls on a striated ground and with lion masks at the shoulders. His cloak is caught up by a narrow scarf which passes over the right shoulder.

Condition: Black lacquer over yellowish bronze.

Henri de La Tour d'Auvergne, Vicomte de Turenne (1611–75), fought with distinction in the Thirty Years' War and became a Marshal of France in 1643. After many successful campaigns, he was killed at Sasbach in 1675 and was buried in Saint-Denis. In 1800 his remains were reinterred by Napoleon in the church of Les Invalides.

Other bronze versions of the present bust, paired with a bust of Louis de Bourbon, the "Grand Condé," are in the Royal collection at Windsor Castle;[1] in the Wallace Collection, London;[2] and in the collection of the Duke of Wellington, Stratfield Saye House, Reading. A version of the Turenne bust alone, without the Condé, is in the Museo de Arte at Ponce, Puerto Rico (formerly in the collection of Dr. A. Hamilton Rice[3]), and a version paired with a bust of Louis XIV was formerly in the Holford collection, Dorchester House, London.[4] Other versions no doubt exist.

In the Salon of 1704 Coysevox exhibited busts of both Condé and Turenne; the material is in neither case specified in the catalogue.[5] Previously he had executed two other busts of Condé, a bronze of 1688 (now in the Louvre) and a terracotta of 1678 (at Chantilly).[6] Both these portraits differ from the bust of Condé paired with the Turenne bust in the collections mentioned above.

The Frick portrait has been attributed to Jérome Derbais, "marbrier," who in 1708 was paid for supplying busts of Condé and Turenne[7] which are still in the château at Chantilly. No original portrait sculptures by Derbais have been recorded, and it can be assumed that these imaginative conceptions could not

84

possibly be the unaided achievement of a relatively obscure "marbrier." Derbais must, therefore, have copied in marble two existing busts, very probably the ones Coysevox exhibited in the Salon of 1704. It is worth mentioning that at the end of the eighteenth century the Chantilly pair were thought to be by Coysevox and that this ascription was accepted until the record of the payment to Derbais was published in 1892.[8]

When the remains of Marshal Turenne were transferred to Les Invalides in 1800, a number of plaster casts were made of the marble bust at Chantilly.[9] Bronze casts may also have been made, and the existing bronze versions, which, with the exception of the Frick example, agree with the marble in the minutest detail, probably date from this time. The Frick version, however, differs from all others in that the ground of the cuirass is striated and not plain, no portion of the cuirass is visible below the bottom line of the cloak, and the irises of the eyes are indicated. It is also more lively than the Derbais bust at Chantilly. It probably ante-dates the Derbais bust, and the possibility that it is the bust of Turenne which Coysevox exhibited in the Salon of 1704 is not excluded.

Collections: Lord Annaly, Holdenby House, Northampton. Frick, 1918.

NOTES

1 Acquired by George IV in 1824.

2 J. G. Mann, *Wallace Collection Catalogues: Sculpture,* London, 1931, p. 62, No. S 164.

3 *Art Journal,* XXV (Pt. 2), 1965–66, p. 169, illustrated advertisement.

4 *The Holford Collection, Dorchester House,* Oxford–London, 1927, II, p. 44, No. 201, Pl. CLXXXII, as Coysevox.

5 J.-J. Guiffrey, *Collection des livrets des anciennes expositions depuis 1673 jusqu'en 1800* (Exposition de 1704), Paris, 1869, p. 10. See also G. Keller-Dorian, *Antoine Coysevox,* Paris, 1920, II, pp. 40–41.

6 Keller-Dorian, *op. cit.,* I, pp. 13, 62–63, Pls. 17, 18, 75.

7 G. Macon (*Les Arts dans la maison de Condé,* Paris, 1903, p. 56) quotes from a document of August 29, 1707: "à Derbais, marbrier, la somme de 2400 livres pour quatre bustes de marbre qu'il a vendus à S.A.S. Mgr le Prince, savoir un buste représentant feu Mgr le Prince, un autre représentant feu M. de Turenne, sans escabellons, et deux autres bustes représentant deux Maures avec leur escabellons."

8 The Derbais document, discovered by G. Macon, was first published by G. Bapst in "Coysevox et le Grand Condé," *Gazette des Beaux-Arts,* 3e pér., VII, 1892, pp. 220, 221.

9 Keller-Dorian, *op. cit.,* II, p. 118.

86

JEAN-LOUIS LEMOYNE

1665–1755

The prodigious working life of Jean-Louis Lemoyne extended from 1685, when he is first mentioned in the royal accounts, until 1740, when ill-health forced him into inactivity. After 1725 he worked in collaboration with his son, Jean-Baptiste II Lemoyne. Many of the early sculptures by Jean-Louis were executed to form part of decorative complexes in the châteaux and gardens of Versailles, Trianon, and Marly. He is responsible also for a few brilliant portraits, notably busts of the architects Jules-Hardouin Mansart and Jacques Gabriel. His masterpiece is a work of his old age, La Crainte des traits de l'Amour, *a marble group now in the Metropolitan Museum, New York.*

Garden Vase (14.2.70)

Executed in 1727–28. Marble: 53 in. (134.6 cm).

Description: The rim of the urn-shaped vase is decorated on the upper surface with a form of egg-and-dart ornament and on the under side with acanthus leaves in low relief. The body of the vase is carved at the top with two female masks in high relief, between which are suspended swags of flowers, fruit, and wheat; below the swags are two handles in the form of dragons which emerge from foliated petal flutings. The stem, which is carved with spiral flutings, is topped by a band of rosette and ribbon ornament and terminates below in a molding of acanthus leaves above a square plinth.

Condition: The surface is much weathered. The dragon heads are modern replacements. The rim has been broken and repaired and several cracks have been filled.

Sold from the Rodolphe Kann collection in 1907 as a work of Edme Bouchardon,[1] the vase was published by Réau[2] in 1927 as by Jean-Louis Lemoyne, with the following extract from the records of the Bâtiments du Roi: "Du 30 janvier 1737. Au Sʳ Le Moyne le père, sculpteur, pour faire le parfait paiement de 2,799 livres à quoy montent les ouvrages de sculpture qu'il a faits à un vase de marbre, pour le service du Roi, pendant les années 1727 et 1728, suivant un mémoire. Ci: 299 liv." According to a *Mémoir des ouvrage de sculpture qui sont au châteaux de la Meut,* in 1746 the vase was in the garden of the royal château of La Muette,

paired with a similar vase by either Charles or Alexandre Rousseau: "Un vaze de marbre blan de 4 pié de haut, orné de deux ance en forme de dragon; sur les milieu dudit vaze son 2 teste aveque des girlandes de blé, fleur et fruit, par M. *Le Moine.* Est à gauche au milieu du parter. – Marbre. De l'autre côté est un parelle vaze, par M. Rousseau – Marbre." It is also recorded[3] that "Au bout du parter est 2 vase de marbre blanc, de 5 pié de haut, orné de feuilles de chesne et autre attribut de chasse, par M. *Rousseau* – Marbre." The ornaments mentioned suggest that the second pair of vases may have represented Winter and that the Lemoyne vase and its companion represented Summer. Also at La Muette in 1746 was Lemoyne's *Compagne de Diane,* now in the National Gallery of Art, Washington.

Two similar but much larger vases (H. 69½ in.; 176.5 cm) with attributes of Autumn, by Pigalle and Nicolas-Sébastien Adam, are in the Metropolitan Museum, New York. They were commissioned for the garden of the château of Choisy in 1742, together with two Spring vases by Jacques Verberckt now in the Louvre and at Malmaison.[4]

Collections: Rodolphe Kann. Duveen. Frick, 1914.

NOTES

1 *Catalogue de la collection Rodolphe Kann: Objets d'art,* Paris, 1907, II, No. 88, reproduced.

2 L. Réau, *Une Dynastie de sculpteurs au XVIIIᵉ siècle: Les Lemoyne,* Paris, 1927, p. 34, No. 18, Pl. LXXX, Fig. 128.

3 *Nouvelles Archives de l'art français,* VIII, 1892, p. 359.

4 J. G. Phillips, "The Choisy-Ménars Vases," *Metropolitan Museum of Art Bulletin,* February 1967, p. 243.

After
FRANÇOIS-JACQUES-JOSEPH SALY
1717–1776

Born at Valenciennes, Saly studied at an early age under Guillaume I Coustou in Paris and was a pupil at the French Academy in Rome from 1740 until 1748. After working in Paris for five years, he settled in Denmark, where he became Director of the Academy and executed his most important sculpture, the bronze equestrian statue of Frederick V in Copenhagen. Saly returned to Paris in 1774 and died there two years later.

Bust of a Young Girl (34.2.84)

Inscribed, diagonally, at the back: *Marest.* Executed in the nineteenth century after a

model of about 1750. Marble: H. of bust 13½ in. (34.3 cm); H. of stand 4⅛ in. (10.5 cm).

Description: The girl looks downward. Her hair is drawn back in three plaits and knotted on the crown of the head with hair drawn up from the nape of the neck.

Condition: The bust is in good condition.

There is no record of a sculptor named Marest. The present marble is a nineteenth century copy of a well-known bust of about 1750, sometimes called *La Boudeuse,* by François-Jacques-Joseph Saly. The Saly bust exists in many examples,[1] notably the following: marble versions in the David-Weill collection at Neuilly-sur-Seine and in the Victoria and Albert Museum, London; terracottas in the Louvre, in the Rijksmuseum, Amsterdam, and in the Ny Carlsberg Glyptotek, Copenhagen; and a bronze in the National Gallery of Art, Washington. The bust is also represented in several works by François Boucher, including a wall panel for Crécy now in The Frick Collection (No. 16.1.10).

The Saly portrait was at one time incorrectly thought to represent Alexandrine d'Étiolles, daughter of Madame de Pompadour.[2] Levey[3] persuasively argues that

92

the subject might instead be the single surviving child of François de Troy, Director of the French Academy in Rome.

Collections: Duveen. Gift of Miss Helen C. Frick, 1934.

NOTES

1 Numerous versions are listed by M. Benisovich in "A Bust of Alexandrine d'Étiolles by Saly," *Gazette des Beaux-Arts,* 6ᵉ pér., XXVIII, 1945, pp. 31–42.

2 The theory is demolished by M. Beaulieu in "La Fillette aux nattes," *Bulletin de la Société de l'histoire de l'art français,* 1955, p. 62.

3 M. Levey, "A New Identity for Saly's 'Bust of a Young Girl,'" *Burlington Magazine,* CVII, 1965, p. 91.

Workshop of
ÉTIENNE-MAURICE FALCONET
1716–1791

Falconet, a pupil of Jean-Baptiste II Lemoyne, was a friend of Diderot and was deeply involved in the aesthetic controversies of his day. He served as director of sculpture at the Sèvres porcelain factory between 1757 and 1766 and is credited with the design of the Sèvres statuettes and groups issued during these years. He received a few official commissions for large-scale sculpture in marble, including garden statues for Madame de Pompadour, but was less favored in this respect than was his contemporary Pigalle. In 1766 Falconet accepted an invitation from Catherine the Great to execute a bronze equestrian statue of Peter the Great in St. Petersburg, a monument which was to prove his greatest work. He remained in Russia for twelve years.

Fidelity Crowning Love (15.2.71)

Executed about 1760. Marble: 18⅝ in. (47.3 cm).

Description: Fidelity, represented as a naked girl, hovers on a stylized cloud in front of Love, represented as a naked youth. He leans forward to take her in his arms. She holds a wreath in her right hand, and with her left she raises a bunch of roses over his head. Her hair is dressed in a plait, bound with a ribbon, and decorated with roses. A wind-blown drapery floats between the two figures. On the oval rocky base are a dog and two billing doves. A projecting tuft of vegetation is used as a support for the left foot of the male figure.

Condition: Both the right hand of Fidelity and the wreath have been broken and reattached.

The present group is closely related to one in the Victoria and Albert Museum, London (H. 19 in.; 48.3 cm),[1] where the right hand of Fidelity rests on the left arm of Love in a restraining gesture and the plait of hair is placed further forward on her head. The identification of the subject is due to Réau,[2] the group having formerly been called *Diana and Endymion*. The pet dog is an attribute of Fidelity and the wreath may symbolize eternity. The group belongs to a class of small marble sculptures which originated in the workshop of Falconet in the 1750s, though no individual example can be ascribed with certainty to Falconet himself. The Frick marble was one of nine such small sculptures in the Pierpont Morgan collection; three of these are now in the Huntington Art Gallery, San Marino, California, and two are in the Museum of Fine Arts, Boston.

Exhibited: London, Victoria and Albert Museum, 1912, No. 1602, lent by J. Pierpont Morgan. Probably New York, Metropolitan Museum, Morgan Collection, 1914, lent by the J. Pierpont Morgan Estate.[3]

Collections:[4] J. Pierpont Morgan, London and New York. Frick, 1915.

NOTES

1 *Victoria and Albert Museum: Catalogue of the Jones Collection,* II, London, 1924, p. 96, No. 371, Pl. 69.
2 L. Réau, *Étienne-Maurice Falconet,* Paris, 1922, I, p. 238, Pl. XVI.
3 *Guide to the Loan Exhibition of the J. Pierpont Morgan Collection,* Metropolitan Museum, New York, 1914, p. 114: "two small groups, the one in marble being by Falconet in a monumental moment."
4 *The Frick Collection Catalogue* (VI, 1954, p. 43) gives the following early provenance, without supporting evidence: Duc de Guise; Sir Edward Henry Scott, fifth Bart. (d. 1883), Westbury Court, Northamptonshire; inherited by his son, Sir Samuel Edward Scott, sixth Bart.

CLODION

1738–1814

Claude Michel, called Clodion, was born at Nancy. He studied in Paris with his uncle, Lambert-Sigisbert Adam, and then with Pigalle. In 1762 he travelled to Rome, where he was a pupil at the French Academy until 1767 and afterwards worked independently. He returned to Paris in 1771 and stayed there almost continuously until 1792, when he withdrew to Nancy for six years. From 1798 until his death he was again in Paris. Although Clodion received some commissions for marble sculpture, his workshops were primarily occupied with architectural reliefs in stone and with the execution of small terracotta statuettes and groups. In his prosperous years, the decade after 1775, Clodion was assisted by three of his brothers and by Joseph-Charles Marin. The chronology of the Clodion terracottas is obscure, but a small number of works executed before 1770 and after 1797 are inscribed with the year in which they were made.

Satyr with Two Bacchantes (16.2.75)

Incised, on the back of the base: CLODIОИ. M. / *in Roma. 1766.* Terracotta: H. 18⅝ in. (47.3 cm).

Description: A drunken bacchante, naked except for a strip of drapery passing over her right arm and left thigh, holds aloft a bunch of grapes with her right hand as she reels against a satyr, who supports her from behind and fondles her left breast. A goatskin passes over the satyr's right shoulder and right thigh. An infant satyr, his left hand in that of the bacchante, capers on her left. A second bacchante, wearing a goatskin over the left shoulder and a flowing gown, supports her companion with the left hand and proffers a cup with the right. On the ground lie a thyrsus and a tambourine with grapes and vine leaves.

Condition: The group has been damaged and repaired in several places. Fractures have occurred in the left leg and the lower right arm of the satyr, in the lower left leg and the raised arm of the central bacchante, and in the right leg of the second bacchante. The cup has been broken off and rejoined, and the left horn of the satyr is a reconstruction in plaster. Damaged areas have been painted over in opaque watercolor; elsewhere the surface of the terracotta remains exposed.

The high regard accorded Clodion's work while he was attending the French Academy in Rome is recorded in letters of April 16 and July 16, 1766,[1] from Charles Natoire, the Director, to the Marquis de Marigny. In the first of these Natoire writes: "Le s^r Claudion, sculpteur, m'a fait voir une suitte de petit modelle qui sont fort bien."

Another signed terracotta inscribed with the same date as the present group, 1766, and representing *Minerva,* was recorded in 1911 in a French private collection.[2] Also in the same early manner is a group representing *Silenus with Two Bacchantes,* signed and dated 1768, which was sold from the Charles E. Dunlap collection in 1963.[3]

Collections: C. de Camondo, Paris (1893).[4] Comtesse de Béarn, Paris (1899).[5] J. Pierpont Morgan, London and New York. Frick, 1916.

NOTES

1 A. de Montaiglon and J.-J. Guiffrey, *Correspondance des directeurs de l'Académie de France à Rome,* XII, Paris, 1902, pp. 114, 119.

2 S. Lami, *Dictionnaire des sculpteurs de l'école française au dix-huitième siècle,* Paris, 1911, II, p. 144.

3 Charles E. Dunlap sale, April 13, 1963, Parke-Bernet, Lot 143. Previously in the Collection V..... sale, June 27–28, 1924, Hôtel Drouot, Paris, Lot 70.

4 Camondo sale (anonymous), February 1–3, 1893, Galerie Georges Petit, Paris, Lot 250.

5 *Le Dix-huitième Siècle: Les Moeurs, les arts, les idées: Récits et témoignages contemporains,* Paris, 1899, repr. p. 111.

Zephyrus and Flora (15.2.76)

Incised, on the back of the base: CLODION. / 1799. Terracotta: H. 20¾ in. (52.7 cm).

Description: Flora, naked except for a garland of roses passing over the right shoulder and a strip of drapery over the left, exchanges an embrace with Zephyrus, who holds a wreath of roses over her head. Their lips almost touch. He has butterfly wings and is naked except for a wind-blown strip of drapery passing over the right shoulder and across the left thigh. Flora is attended by three putti: one, poised with the left foot on the ground, touches her right leg with both hands, urging her towards Zephyrus; a second holds a basket of flowers; and the third takes roses from the basket and scatters them on the ground. The two putti with flowers are supported by billowing clouds. Zephyrus stands on a flat cloud which overlaps the oval base.

Condition: Both wings of the uppermost putto are replacements, rendered as butterfly wings but probably originally bird wings similar to those of the other two putti; the left leg of the same putto has been restored in plaster. The left wing and left hand of Zephyrus and the wreath he holds have been broken off and reattached. There are fire cracks between the right arm of Flora and the waist of Zephyrus and between his left hip and the adjacent drapery.

Although hitherto known as *Cupid and Psyche* or *The Embrace,* the subject is defined by the youth's butterfly wings, which are an attribute of Zephyrus, and by the girl's garland of roses, an attribute of Flora, coupled with the scattering of roses, an activity of Flora.[1]

The composition of the group appears to be foreshadowed in the *Bacchus and a Bacchante* in the Dutuit Collection, Petit Palais, Paris, which, though undated, seems on stylistic grounds to be earlier, and by a very similar group of the same subject in the Metropolitan Museum, New York (Altman Bequest). Another terracotta by Clodion signed and dated 1799 is *La Surprise* in the National Gallery of Art, Washington.[2]

102

Exhibited: New York, Metropolitan Museum, 1914, lent by the J. Pierpont Morgan Estate.[3]

Collections: J. Pierpont Morgan, London and New York. Frick, 1915.

NOTES

1 For other representations of Zephyrus and Flora, see A. Pigler, *Barockthemen,* Budapest, 1956, II, pp. 256–58.

2 *Summary Catalogue of European Paintings and Sculpture,* Washington, 1965, p. 149, No. A-145.

3 *Guide to the Loan Exhibition of the J. Pierpont Morgan Collection,* Metropolitan Museum, New York, 1914, p. 114.

LOUIS-SIMON BOIZOT

1743–1809

After studying under René-Michel (Michelange) Slodtz, Boizot was a pupil at the French Academy in Rome from 1765 until 1770. Throughout his working life he was well supplied with commissions for public monuments, tombs, architectural reliefs, and portraits, but his most important activity was his service from 1774 until 1800 as director of sculpture at the Sèvres porcelain factory, a post held at an earlier date by Falconet.

Peter Adolf Hall (15.2.72)

Executed probably in 1775. Terracotta: H. 19 in. (48.3 cm).

Description: Hall's head is turned to his right. His hair is combed back from the brow, dressed in a tight curl over each ear, and tied in a queue at the back. His coat is open at the neck, revealing a frilled unbuttoned shirt.

Condition: In 1963, the bust was restored and dirt was removed from parts of the surface. The lower edge of the bust, which had previously been repaired, was retouched in watercolor.

Peter Adolf Hall, a distinguished painter of miniatures, was born at Borås, Sweden, in 1739. He lived in Paris for most of his working life, but left during the Revolutionary years. He died at Liège in 1793. Two miniature self-portraits by Hall are in the National Museum, Stockholm.[1]

The Frick bust of Hall was for many years ascribed to Pajou, although Stein[2] and Maclagan[3] noted that it differed in character from the Pajou bust of Madame Hall now also in The Frick Collection (see following entry). The ascription of Hall's bust to Boizot was first advanced by the editors of *The Frick Collection Catalogue*[4] on grounds of style, citing the analogy of the Sèvres busts of Paul I, Comte du Nord (1781), and Necker (1789).[5] This attribution is reinforced by the fact that in a 1778 inventory of works of art in Hall's house there appears the following entry: "Boizot. – Mon buste et celui de ma femme en terre cuite."[6] The same inventory also lists the Pajou bust of Madame Hall—which, together with the present bust, passed through the collections of Hall's descendants—but no

bust of Hall by Pajou is recorded. The Boizot bust of Madame Hall has disappeared.

It is possible that the present bust can be identified with the Boizot entry No. 267 in the catalogue of the Salon of 1775: "Le portrait de M. Hallé, Peintre du Roi. Buste en terre cuite."[7] No bust by Boizot of Noël Hallé, who was sixty-four years old in 1775, is known, and as Hall also was *Peintre du Roi,* the spelling of the name in the catalogue may be incorrect. The bust of Hall is certainly of about this date.

Collections: Peter Adolf Hall, Paris. By descent to his grandnephew, the Marquis de la Grange. Colonel Boyer. Lowengard, Paris. Duveen (1912).[8] Frick, 1915.

NOTES

1 K. Asplund, "Peter Adolf Hall: en biografisk skiss," *Nationalmusei Årsbok,* 1938, pp. 45, 63, Figs. 14, 25.

2 H. Stein, *Augustin Pajou,* Paris, 1912, pp. 43–44.

3 E. Maclagan, in *The Frick Collection Catalogue,* VI, 1954, p. 46.

4 *Loc. cit.*

5 E. Bourgeois and G. Lechevallier-Chevignard, *Le Biscuit de Sèvres,* I, Paris, 1913 Pls. 46, 55.

6 F. Villot, *Hall: Sa Vie, ses oeuvres, sa correspondance,* Paris, 1867, p. 80.

7 J.-J. Guiffrey, *Collection des livrets des anciennes expositions depuis 1673 jusqu'en 1800* (Exposition de 1775), Paris, 1870, p. 39, No. 267.

8 Stein, *op. cit.,* p. 43, note 5.

AUGUSTIN PAJOU

1730–1809

Pajou, a pupil of Jean-Baptiste II Lemoyne, went to the French Academy in Rome in 1752. Returning to France in 1756, he became a successful court sculptor, now best remembered for his portraits of Madame du Barry. He also designed interior settings, the most important of which was for the theater in the château of Versailles. He continued to play a part in official life during and after the Revolution.

Marie-Adélaïde Hall (15.2.73)

Inscribed, at the back: *Pajou | fe | 1775.* Terracotta: H. 24⅞ in. (63.2 cm).

Description: Madame Hall looks to her right. Her hair is elaborately dressed in heavy plaits and curls, with one looped plait resting on the right shoulder. Over a low shift she wears drapery suspended from the left shoulder and falling below the right breast, leaving the right shoulder bare.

Condition: The bust was cleaned in 1963. The surface of the terracotta, which had been disturbed, has been painted in opaque watercolor.

The sitter, who was the daughter of a Versailles merchant named Gobin, was married to Peter Adolf Hall, the painter of miniatures, in 1771. A portrait bust of her husband by Boizot is now also in The Frick Collection (see preceding entry), but a pendant portrait by Boizot of Madame Hall has disappeared. Hall portrayed Madame Hall with her sister and daughter in a miniature of 1776, now in the Wallace Collection, London.[1]

The present bust is mentioned in an inventory of works of art in the house of Peter Hall, drawn up in 1778: "Pajou – Le buste de ma femme en terre cuite."[2] In 1790 it appears in an inventory of works of art in the living room of Madame Hall, this time with a bust by Pajou of Jean-Jacques Rousseau.[3] There is no record that Pajou ever made a portrait of Peter Hall.

Pajou's portrait of Madame Hall may have been exhibited in the Salon of 1775, the date with which it is inscribed. That year Pajou showed "Plusieurs Bustes, dont un en marbre,"[4] but the sitters' names are not listed in the catalogue.

Stein[5] comments on the present portrait, "C'est une femme de quarante ans, qui rachète par la noblesse du port ce que la nature lui avait refusé en beauté." Madame Hall was in fact about twenty-five when the bust was made.

Collections: Peter Adolf Hall, Paris. By descent to his grandnephew, the Marquis de la Grange. Colonel Boyer. Lowengard, Paris. Duveen (1912).[6] Frick, 1915.

NOTES

1 *Wallace Collection Catalogues: Miniatures and Illuminations,* London, 1935, p. 72, No. M 186, Pl. 18.

2 F. Villot, *Hall: Sa Vie, ses oeuvres, sa correspondance,* Paris, 1867, p. 80.

3 K. Asplund, "Peter Adolf Hall: en biografisk skiss," *Nationalmusei Årsbok,* 1938, pp. 64–67.

4 J.-J. Guiffrey, *Collection des livrets des anciennes expositions depuis 1673 jusqu'en 1800* (Exposition de 1775), Paris, 1870, p. 34, No. 223.

5 H. Stein, *Augustin Pajou,* Paris, 1912, p. 44.

6 *Idem,* p. 43, note 5.

JEAN-ANTOINE HOUDON

1741–1828

Houdon studied initially under René-Michel (Michelange) Slodtz. In 1764 he went to the French Academy in Rome, where he executed several large-scale works including an early masterpiece, the marble figure of St. Bruno *in the church of S. Maria degli Angeli. He returned to Paris in 1768 and, in the absence of orders for official sculpture, became increasingly occupied with portrait busts. The majority of his large-scale works were executed for private or foreign patrons, including a commission for the statue of George Washington now in the Capitol at Richmond, Virginia. Houdon was deeply expert in the study of anatomy and in the techniques of the sculpture workshop. He was the first sculptor to reproduce his own works in quantity, busts of famous men being multiplied in marble, terracotta, plaster, and bronze. He has been generally regarded by posterity as the greatest sculptor of the eighteenth century and the greatest portrait sculptor of all time.*

Comtesse du Cayla (16.2.77)

Inscribed, on the back of the stand: A. HOUDON, F. AN. 1777. Marble: H. of bust 21 ¼ in. (54 cm); H. of stand 5⅝ in. (14.3 cm).

Description: The Countess looks to her left. Her hair is decorated with roses. She wears a sleeveless gown, fastened with a clasp on the left shoulder, and a garland of vine leaves falling across her breast from the right shoulder. The bust and the quadrangular molded stand are carved separately in white marble with gray flecks.

Condition: Three corners of the stand are chipped.

Élisabeth-Susanne (1755–1816), daughter of Louis-Pierre, Comte de Jaucourt, was married in 1772 to François-Hercule-Philippe-Étienne de Baschi, Comte du Cayla. Towards the end of her life she became lady-in-waiting to Louise-Marie-Joséphine of Savoy, the Queen of Louis XVIII.

114

The present portrait was exhibited in the Salon of 1777,[1] under "Bustes en marbre," as: "239. Portrait de Madame la Comtesse de Cayla." A plaster version had been exhibited in 1775[2] as: "255. Le Buste de Mme. la Comtesse du Caila." In the Salon of 1777 Houdon also exhibited a posthumous marble bust of the Comtesse de Jaucourt (d. 1774), the mother of the Comtesse du Cayla. The two marble busts, which are of about the same size and which face in opposite directions, may have been designed as companions; they remained in the collections of the Jaucourt family until after 1884. The bust of Madame de Jaucourt, previously in the David-Weill collection, was given to the Louvre in 1937.[3]

In about 1784, Houdon himself compiled a list of works he had executed after 1769. Under the year 1777 appear: "No. 38. Le buste en marbre de Mad. la comtesse de Jaucourt," and "No. 39. Le buste en marbre de Mad. la comtesse de Caylas."[4]

When shown at the Salon, the marble bust of Madame du Cayla was drawn by Gabriel de Saint-Aubin in the margin of his exhibition catalogue, with the comment: "admirable pour la légèreté du ciseau."[5] Commenting on the Salon of 1775, the author of the *Mémoires secrets*[6] remarked of the plaster version: "On voit dans Madame la comtesse *du Caila,* la douce ivresse, la gaité vive, l'abandon folâtre d'une Bacchante, au commencement d'une orgie, dans les premiers accès du plaisir, comme cela devoit être, pour lui accorder quelque noblesse et quelque décence."

The bust was described by Maclagan[7] as "one of the outstanding masterpieces of the greatest of eighteenth-century sculptors" and by Vitry[8] as "étincelant de grâce vivante." Arnason[9] remarked on its rococo character, in contrast to Houdon's practically contemporary statue of *Diana,* of which the terracotta version is now in The Frick Collection (No. 39.2.79). Réau[10] suggested that the representation of the subject as a bacchante is an allusion to her husband's family name, Baschi; the supporters of the family's coat of arms were a Bacchus and a bacchante.[11]

Exhibited: Paris, Salon of 1777, No. 239. Paris, Palais du Corps législatif, Exposition en faveur de l'oeuvre des Alsaciens et Lorrains, 1874, lent by the Marquis de Jaucourt.[12] Paris, Exposition de l'art au XVIIIᵉ siècle, 1884, No. 256, lent by the Marquis de Jaucourt.[13]

Collections: Jaucourt family (until after 1884). Jacques Seligmann. Joseph Bardac. Wildenstein and Gimpel. Frick, 1916.

1 J.-J. Guiffrey, *Collection des livrets des anciennes expositions depuis 1673 jusqu'en 1800* (Exposition de 1777), Paris, 1870, p. 45.

2 *Idem* (Exposition de 1775), p. 38.

3 L. Réau, *Houdon: Sa Vie et son oeuvre,* Paris, 1964, Pt. III, p. 319.

4 *Idem,* Pt. I, p. 95.

5 É. Dacier, *Gabriel de Saint-Aubin,* I, Paris, 1929, p. 104, Pl. XXXIII. The complete catalogue, with the drawings by Saint-Aubin, is reproduced in *Catalogues de ventes et livrets de salons illustrés par Gabriel de Saint-Aubin,* ed. É. Dacier, III, Paris, 1910.

6 L. Petit de Bachaumont, *Mémoires secrets pour servir à l'histoire de la République des lettres en France depuis 1762 jusqu'à nos jours,* XIII, London, 1780, p. 181 (letter of September 29, 1775).

7 In *The Frick Collection Catalogue,* VI, 1954, p. 53.

8 P. Vitry, in A. Michel, *Histoire de l'art,* VII (Pt. 2), 1924, p. 585.

9 H. Arnason, *Sculpture by Houdon: A Loan Exhibition,* Worcester (Massachusetts) Art Museum, 1964, pp. 5–6.

10 *Op. cit.,* Pt. II, p. 319.

11 F. A. Aubert de la Chenaye des Bois, *Dictionnaire de la noblesse,* II, 1863, p. 447.

12 P. Mantz, "Exposition en faveur de l'oeuvre des Alsaciens et Lorrains," *Gazette des Beaux-Arts,* 2ᵉ pér., X, 1874, p. 308.

13 A. de Montaiglon, "Signatures et inscriptions des sculptures de l'Exposition de l'art au XVIIIᵉ siècle," *Nouvelles Archives de l'art français,* 3ᵉ sér., I, 1884–85, pp. 39–40.

Armand-Thomas Hue, Marquis de Miromesnil (35.2.78)

Inscribed, on the back of the bust: A. T. HUE ... DE MIROMENIL. FAIT PAR HOUDON EN 1777. Marble: H. of bust 25½ in. (64.8 cm); H. of stand 6¾ in. (17.2 cm).

Description: The head of the Marquis is turned slightly to his left. He wears a heavy wig and the dress of a magistrate. His gown falls open to reveal neck tabs, a robe with a row of buttons, and a sash of office tied in a large bow, which half protrudes from the gown on his left. The quadrangular molded stand is carved in gray marble.

Condition: The word MARQUIS has been excised from the inscription (see discussion below), presumably during the Revolutionary years.

Armand-Thomas Hue, fourth Marquis de Miromesnil (or Miroménil), was born in 1723 of an ancient Norman family which had been raised to the nobility in the sixteenth century. In 1757 he became *Premier Président* of the Norman *Parlement* in Rouen. On the accession of Louis XVI he was appointed *Garde des Sceaux* (Minister of Justice), receiving his seals of office on August 24, 1774. In 1781 he was awarded the Order of the Saint-Esprit. After his retirement in 1787 he lived on his estate at Miromesnil, near Dieppe. He was imprisoned briefly by Revolutionaries in 1794, afterwards returning to Miromesnil, where he died in 1796.

The Frick bust is mentioned in a guide of 1866[1] as being in the château of Bretteville (Seine-Inférieure). This château had formerly belonged to Charles Cardin le Bret, husband of the sitter's eldest daughter. At the death of Cardin le Bret, Bretteville and its contents passed to his nephew, the Marquis de Flers, and at the latter's death they passed to his nephew, Henri de Courtivron, from whom the bust was acquired by Wildenstein before 1919.

Three additional versions of the portrait exist, two in marble[2] and one in plaster as follows:

120

1. Marble bust in the Victoria and Albert Museum, London (A. 19-1963), inscribed in letters similar to those on the Frick bust: A. T. HUE MARQUIS DE MIROMENIL GARDE DES SCEAUX. HOUDON F. 1775. This is the bust listed in the catalogue of the Salon of 1775[3] as: "253 – Le Buste de M. le Marquis de Miromesnil, Garde des Sceaux." The material is not specified in the catalogue, but a contemporary comment states that it was marble (see below). When the bust appeared with a Paris dealer in 1898, nothing could be said of its provenance except that it was believed to have come from the Goulaine family in Normandy.[4] It was later in a private collection in Connecticut[5] and in the collections of Baron Cassel van Doorn[6] and René Fribourg,[7] being bought by the Museum from the latter's estate in 1963. The nose has been fractured (apparently long ago) and a flaw in the marble has produced a fissure in the left shoulder.

2. Marble bust in the Musée Fabre, Montpellier, bequeathed by Madame Bouisson in 1893, not inscribed.[8] In this version the subject wears the ribbon of an order (the decoration itself has been effaced), and there are traces on the gown of an embroidered emblem. As the missing order must have been the Saint-Esprit, which the Marquis was awarded in February of 1781, the Montpellier version cannot have been executed before this date. Some authorities have identified the sitter incorrectly as the Abbé Jacques-Denis Cochin and as Armand-Jérôme Bignon.[9]

3. Bronzed plaster bust in the Musée de Peinture et de Sculpture at Orléans, given by Madame Limay (née Desfriches) in 1825, not inscribed.[10] The subject wears no order.

In *The Frick Collection Catalogue*[11] it was proposed that the three marble busts were three separate likenesses, showing the sitter as he appeared, respectively, in 1775, 1777, and 1781, and that the plaster version was datable after 1777 and before 1781. However, the differences in the features are too insignificant to support this hypothesis. Indeed, the notion that Houdon would deliberately make minute alterations at intervals of two and four years to denote the process of aging is inherently improbable in formal portraiture of this kind, as is the implication that he would execute at least three different likenesses with the same posture and substantially the same accessories. The probability is that the Marquis de Miromesnil sat to Houdon for his portrait when he was appointed Garde des Sceaux and that all three marble busts were based on the model executed at that time.

The bust of 1775 in the Victoria and Albert Museum and that of 1777 in The Frick Collection, both fully signed and dated and both of the highest quality, must have been executed personally by Houdon. The main differences between them, apart from the above-mentioned fracture and flaw in the 1775 bust, lie in the forehead and in the eyes. There are furrows on the brow of the 1775 bust that are omitted in the Frick version, and although the device for giving expression to the eyes is essentially the same in both busts—a deep boring in the center of a circular excavation overlapped by the eyelid—the excavation in the earlier version is more irregular and the rim round the boring less distinct than in the Frick version.

In the list Houdon compiled in about 1784 of works he had executed since 1769,[12] the Frick version is mentioned under the year 1777 ("No. 50. Le buste de marbre de Mr de Miroménil, garde des sceaux de France"), but the London version of 1775 is not mentioned at all, although it was this bust that had been shown in the Salon. According to the catalogue of Houdon's posthumous sale in 1828,[13] a marble bust of Miromesnil was still in the sculptor's possession at his death. These two facts suggest the possibility that the 1777 bust was a replacement for that of 1775, perhaps because of the flaw in the marble or the fractured nose, and that the earlier bust thereafter remained in the sculptor's possession. However, this is conjectural. Brière[14] formed the opinion that it was the Montpellier bust that remained with the sculptor.

Commenting on the Salon of 1775, the author of *Mémoires secrets*[15] wrote as follows: "M. de Miromesnil est très ressemblant, mais lourdement vêtu; sa simarre a ces plis roides & durs que l'art doit éviter si soigneusement, & la perruque surtout est d'un volume énorme; c'est un bloc de marbre dont il est écrasé, non encore dégrossi. Il est vrai que cet ornement est tout-à-fait ingrat. La chevelure ondoyante de M. Turgot[16] est plus avantageuse & aussi mieux rendue...."

In 1774 a subscription was opened in Rouen for the erection in the Palais de Justice of a full-length statue of Miromesnil,[17] but there is no evidence that any statue was erected. In Houdon's inventory of about 1784, No. 23 (undated) is: "Medaillon de Mad. de Miroménil"; this portrait has not been identified.[18]

Collections: Madame le Bret, Château de Bretteville, Seine-Inférieure. Marquis de Flers. Henri de Courtivron. Wildenstein. C. Ledyard Blair (1919). Wildenstein. Frick, 1935.

1 A. Joanne, *Itinéraire-général de la France: Normandie,* Paris, 1866, p. 148: "Le château... renferme un remarquable buste en marbre blanc, sculpté par Houdon (1777), représentant le marquis de Miromesnil, garde des sceaux de Louis XVI, et propriétaire de cette élégante demeure seigneuriale."

2 L. Réau (*Houdon: Sa Vie et son oeuvre,* Paris, 1964, Pt. II, p. 326, Pt. III, p. 37, No. 163) incorrectly lists three additional versions in marble.

3 J.-J. Guiffrey, *Collection des livrets des anciennes expositions depuis 1673 jusqu'en 1800* (Exposition de 1775), Paris, 1870, p. 38.

4 G. Brière, "Notes sur quelques bustes de Houdon," *Nouvelles Archives de l'art français,* 4ᵉ sér., VII, 1913, p. 350.

5 Lilli Wulf and others sale, February 9–10, 1951, Parke-Bernet, Lot 311. According to the sale catalogue, this version was owned previously by E. Lowengard, Paris (1906), and Mrs. W. K. Vanderbilt, Paris.

6 His sale, December 9–10, 1955, Parke-Bernet, Lot 272.

7 His sale, October 17–18, 1963, Sotheby's, Lot 733.

8 Particulars of the Montpellier marble and the Orléans plaster are given by Brière (*op. cit.,* pp. 352–53) and by Réau (*op. cit.,* Pt. III, p. 37, No. 163). According to Réau, both busts were exhibited in the 1928 Houdon centenary exhibition in the Bibliothèque de Versailles under No. 33.

9 Although the Orléans version is correctly identified as Miromesnil by G. Giacometti in *La Vie et l'oeuvre de Houdon* (I, Paris, 1929, p. 168), the Montpellier version, reproduced in profile, is wrongly identified as Bignon (II, p. 10).

10 See note 8. The Orléans bronzed plaster was also shown later in 1928 at the Galeries Buvelot, Paris, No. 49.

11 XII, 1955, pp. 102–03.

12 See Réau, *op. cit.,* Pt. I, p. 96.

13 *Idem,* p. 118, No. 32: "Marbre blanc. Buste de *Hue de Miromesnil,* garde des sceaux, mort le 6 juillet 1793 [sic]."

14 *Op. cit.,* p. 353.

15 L. Petit de Bachaumont, *Mémoires secrets pour servir à l'histoire de la République des lettres en France depuis 1762 jusqu'à nos jours,* XIII, London, 1780, p. 214 (letter of September 29, 1775).

16 A terracotta version of the Turgot bust is in the Boston Museum of Fine Arts. See H. Arnason, *Sculpture by Houdon: A Loan Exhibition,* Worcester (Massachusetts) Art Museum, 1964, p. 40.

17 Petit de Bachaumont, *op. cit.,* VII, 1777, pp. 280–81 (letter of December 7, 1774).

18 See Réau, *op. cit.,* Pt. I, p. 95.

Diana the Huntress (39.2.79)

Inscribed, on the top of the base in the front left corner: HOUDON *Scult* (see below). Executed between 1776 and 1795. Terracotta: H. overall 75½ in. (191.8 cm); H. of figure 68⅛ in. (173 cm).

Description: The naked goddess strides forward, poised on the left foot, with the right foot raised behind her. She turns her head to her right. In her left hand, which is extended downward, she holds a bow; her right hand, which is slightly raised, once held an arrow. Her hair is adorned with a crescent moon. The base is square.

Condition: From visible junctions, the statue appears to be constructed of ten sections separately fired: *(i)* the head, *(ii)* the left arm, *(iii)* the right arm, *(iv)* the upper trunk from the shoulders to just above the navel, *(v)* the lower trunk and thighs, *(vi)* the upper left leg and knee, *(vii)* the upper right leg and knee, *(viii)* the lower right leg and foot, *(ix)* the lower left leg, and *(x)* the left foot; the possibility that there are one or two additional junctions, which are entirely disguised, cannot be excluded. The bow is carved in wood. X-rays reveal separate metal armatures situated as follows: *(i)* passing through the neck into the head, *(ii)* in the left wrist and hand, *(iii)* in the right elbow and upper forearm, *(iv)* joining the upper right leg to the trunk, *(v)* in the lower right leg and foot, and *(vi)* passing throughout the left leg and foot, with a joint in the ankle, and anchoring the figure to the base; the armatures are not interconnected. There are dowels and clamps in the left hand and dowels in the right hand and fingers. Clamps reinforce the junction of the right leg to the lower trunk and thigh. The dowels were inserted by repairers in this century and the same is probably true of the clamps. The entire statue is covered in a buff-colored paint. From local sampling it seems that the paint in most areas is laid directly on the terracotta, although on the top of the head there are apparently two intermediate coats, pale red above and dark red below. It is conceivable that when the statue was stripped and repainted in 1910–11 it was decided not to strip the existing coats of paint from the hair. The only radical repairs recorded were executed by Léon André in Paris in 1910–11.[1] The entry in his ledger for February 24, 1911, is as follows: "Mme Sardou [a previous owner] – Statue en terre cuite par Houdon diane grandeur naturelle. Enlevé la couche de peinture qui la recouvrait agrafé les membres ebranles, refait les doigts de platre en terre cuite, l'arc et les flèches en bois, rebouché toutes les fentes et les défauts donné aux parties rechargies en plâtre une teinte dans le ton de la terre cuite et harmonisé l'ensemble. Pour transport reparation et frais divers 1250 reçu." When André supplied a photograph of this ledger entry in January of 1939, he wrote as follows: "Je soussigné, Léon André, réparateur des Musées Nationaux, demeurant à Paris, 15 rue Dufrénoy, déclare que la statue en terre cuite de Diane par Houdon, dont photographie ci-contre, est celle qui faisait partie de la Collection de l'auteur dramatique Victorien Sardou. Sur la demande de Madame Victorien Sardou je suis allé, dans le courant de 1910, voir cette statue à Marly, au chateau de la famille Sardou, où elle se trouvait dans l'orangerie et l'ai fait transporter à mes ateliers à Paris. Cette statue en terre cuite est faite par sections reliées entre elles par des armatures métalliques, elle a été reprise à l'époque dans les ateliers de Houdon qui a réparé en plâtre les jonctions et surchargé de même les parties amaigries par le retrait dû à la cuisson. La signature sur la base est originale. J'ai exécuté les travaux de remise en état de la statue, selon détails portés sur mes livres, dont photo annexée." From these statements it is evident that the fingers are replacements, that the bow and the arrow (the latter since removed from the right hand) date from 1910–11, and that the visible paint covering must date from 1910–11 or later, depending on the exact meaning of the word "harmonisé." André also testifies that the portions of the statue that had shrunk too much in the firing had been made up in plaster in the sculptor's workshop; the existence of these patches of plaster make-up and of the junctions implies that the statue must, from the first, have been painted to disguise the blemishes and additions. In a letter of December 11, 1938, Duveen Brothers gives the information that the base, having been damaged, had been strengthened with plaster at an unspecified date. This damage may explain the unsatisfactory nature of the inscription, of which only the H and the first O appear to be authentic. In 1939 cracks in the left ankle and wrist were filled in and toned by Duveen Brothers. In 1951, because of fractures across the thumb and forefinger of the left hand, the metal dowel located in this hand was replaced; at the same time a fracture across the lower part of the bow was repaired. Giacometti[2] records that Victorien Sardou, owner of the statue from about 1869 until his death in 1908, "regrettait...d'en avoir dissimulé avec du mastic l'éclatante nudité; il s'en excusait par la présence constante de ses jeunes fils au logis." André seems to have left this small modification undisturbed.

Only one contemporary reference to a life-size terracotta version of the *Diana* is known. This occurs in the Houdon sale catalogue of 1795:[3] "TERRES CUITES. 86. Diane. Figure de 6 pieds [approximately 76¾ in.; 195 cm] de haut, compris l'épaisseur du socle." The buyer is unknown. While this work probably is the statue now in The Frick Collection, the history of the Frick terracotta can be traced with certainty only to the 1860s, when it belonged to Henry de Montault, director of the *Journal illustré*. There is no confirmation of the tradition that it belonged formerly to Cardinal Fesch[4] and it is not included in any of the Fesch sale catalogues. From Henry de Montault the terracotta passed to Susse, the bronze founder, and from him to Victorien Sardou, the playwright, apparently in 1869. The circumstances of these transfers are unclear, inasmuch as a letter to

Sardou from Henry de Montault implies that he still had some title to the statue while it was in the custodianship of Susse: "1ᵉʳ Septembre 69. Monsieur et illustre Maître, Vous avez acheté chez Susse la Diane de houdon qui m'appartenait et que j'avais deposé chez lui, parceque mes locataires alarmés dans leur pudeur de la voir dans l'escalier de ma maison de l'avenue de l'Impératrice, avaient reclamés ce sacrifice. Je fais un appel a votre camaraderie pour savoir ce que vous l'avez payé? Je n'ai pû le savoir de Mʳ Susse. De plus je sais que Mʳ Susse se passant de mon autorisation à fait faire un moulage de ladite statue.[5] Il est vrai que s'il me l'eut demandé je l'aurais refusé car le Louvre n'a jamais voulu autoriser le moulage du bronze qu'il possède, – non plusque le Musée de l'Hermitage a Pétersbourg qui en une reproduction en marbre. J'attends avec impatience votre reponse, heureux si elle me rappelle a votre souvenir et je me dis, Monsieur, avec toute l'admiration et le respect imaginable, votre très dévoué, Henry de Montault du Jᵃˡ illustré 30, Rue de Londres." Sardou kept the terracotta until his death in 1908. In 1910 it was seen in André's Paris workshop by W. L. Hatfield, "bronzier des musées nationaux," who in 1911 negotiated the sale of the statue by Madame Sardou and her son Jean to Duveen. In August of 1915 it was shipped to America in the steamer *Espagne*. It was sold to The Frick Collection in 1939.

Four additional life-size versions of the *Diana*—one in plaster, one in marble, and two in bronze, all made in the workshop of Houdon—are in existence, as well as a posthumous bronze version which was cast from a plaster by Houdon.[6] Two recorded life-size versions, a plaster and a lead, have disappeared. Particulars are as follows:

1. Plaster version in the Schlossmuseum, Schloss Friedendstein, Gotha, inscribed: *Houdon F. 1776.*[7] This is the earliest version of the *Diana* and must be a replica of the "plâtre original," which the sculptor would have retained in his studio. H. overall 83 in. (210.8 cm); H. of figure 75 in. (190.8 cm).

2. Marble version in the Gulbenkian collection, Palácio Pombal, Oeiras, Portugal, signed and dated: *J. A. Houdon 1780.*[8] In this version only, a quiver hangs at Diana's left side, from a thong passing across the breast and over the right shoulder, and a tuft of reeds at her left serves to support the figure; some form of external support was unavoidable in the marble version, which, unlike the plaster, terracotta, and bronze versions, could not be fitted with an armature. The marble version, originally intended for the Duke of Saxe-Gotha, was sold

130

instead to Catherine the Great owing to the intervention of Grimm, who pointed to the danger of transport overland whereas the statue could travel to St. Petersburg by water. Passing later to the Hermitage Museum, it was sold to Calouste Gulbenkian in 1930. H. overall 82$^{11}/_{16}$ in. (210 cm); H. of figure 76$^{3}/_{16}$ in. (193.5 cm).

3. Bronze version in the Huntington Art Gallery, San Marino, California, inscribed: HOUDON F. 1782 and *Pour J^N* GIRARDOT DE MARIGNY.[9] Commissioned by Girardot de Marigny, to whom was also supplied Houdon's bronze statue of *Apollo* now in the Gulbenkian collection, this version of the *Diana* was subsequently in the collections of Comte Aguado, Lord Hertford, Sir Richard Wallace, and Sir John Murray Scott, all of Paris; Charles T. Yerkes of New York; and Eduardo Guinlé of Rio de Janeiro. H. overall 82$^{5}/_{16}$ in. (209 cm); H. of figure 76$^{9}/_{16}$ in. (194.5 cm).

4. Bronze version in the Louvre, inscribed: HOUDON. F. 1790.[10] Included in the Houdon sale catalogue of 1795, it was unsold and remained in the sculptor's possession. After appearing in the posthumous sale of 1828, it was bought for the Louvre in 1829. It has been alleged that this version was later modified, as was the terracotta version, through motives of modesty. H. overall 82$^{5}/_{16}$ in. (209 cm); H. of figure 76$^{3}/_{4}$ in. (195 cm).

5. Posthumous bronze version in the Musée de Tours, inscribed: *Houdon 1776* and stamped: CARBONNEAUX 1839.[11] This version was presumably cast from a plaster similar to the one at Gotha. It was given to the Tours Museum by Madame Baron in 1884. H. overall 81$^{11}/_{16}$ in. (207.5 cm); H. of figure 74$^{13}/_{16}$ in. (190 cm).

6. Lead version, dimensions unspecified but probably life-size.[12] Included under the year 1781 in the list of his works which Houdon compiled in about 1784, this version has disappeared.

7. Painted plaster version, allegedly cast from the Louvre bronze, included in the posthumous sale of 1828.[13] This also has disappeared. The possibility that this was in fact the "plâtre original" and that it was subsequently used for casting the Tours bronze cannot be excluded.

Numerous busts of the *Diana* and reduced versions exist.

The method Houdon used for constructing large-scale terracotta statues was described by Giacometti[14] in relation to the sculptor's seated *Voltaire* in the Musée Fabre, Montpellier. The clay is pressed into molds taken from the "plâtre original," itself, of course, a cast from the original clay model, which would be destroyed.

The clay positive is then baked in sections. After firing, the sections are assembled and the junctions disguised. Inevitably the sculptor has to carry out a good deal of retouching, because of the junctions and because of the uneven shrinkage of the clay. Evidence of such retouching on the *Diana* was discovered by André when he stripped the paint from the statue in 1910–11 (see *Condition* above).

That the terracotta could have been modelled, as suggested in *The Frick Collection Catalogue,*[15] rather than cast, cannot be accepted. A clay model of the *Diana* would require as support a complete metal armature from top to toe and extending along the arms. In the oven the metal would expand, while the clay would shrink, and the model (even if divided into sections) would be shattered. Yet it would be impossible to remove such an armature before firing. In the Frick *Diana* the local armatures revealed by X-rays were fitted after firing into cavities formed in the cast. These armatures serve to strengthen the terracotta at its weakest points, but they would have been insufficient support for a model in unbaked clay.

Excluding the terracotta, the dimensions of the life-size versions (as recently supplied by the museums and galleries to which they now belong) are fairly close. Taking the heights of the figures alone—without the bases, which vary in thickness—the greatest difference is between the height given for the Gotha plaster, 75 in. (190.8 cm), and that given for the Louvre bronze, 76³/₄ in. (195 cm). The terracotta is substantially smaller—between nine and ten percent—than all the others, having a height, without the base, of 68¹/₈ in. (173 cm), but this can be explained by the normal rate of shrinkage of a terracotta in firing, which is in fact approximately ten percent. Thus it is possible that all the life-size versions depend ultimately from a single "plâtre original."

Altogether, five life-size or nearly life-size statues in terracotta by Houdon are recorded: a seated *Voltaire,* dated 1781, formerly owned by Beaumarchais and now in the Institut et Musée Voltaire at Geneva;[16] the above-mentioned seated *Voltaire,* also dated 1781 (with a chair in reinforced plaster), in the Musée Fabre, Montpellier;[17] a version of *La Frileuse*[18] and a *Baigneuse* (partly in terracotta and partly in plaster),[19] both of which have disappeared; and The Frick Collection's *Diana.*

There is no way of dating the terracotta *Diana* exactly, but it may well have been executed soon after Houdon had gained experience from casting and firing

the Voltaire statues of 1781. The Montpellier *Voltaire* and the missing terracotta *Frileuse* were included in the Houdon sale of 1795, and it is virtually certain that the above-mentioned Lot 86 in that sale was The Frick Collection's *Diana*. No other life-size terracotta version of the *Diana* has ever been recorded.

Although the construction and the finishing of any life-size statue in terracotta involve a number of complex and delicate procedures, the pose of the *Diana* presents quite exceptional problems of balance and support. The Frick Collection's statue is an example of technical virtuosity that surpasses anything else achieved by Houdon in this material, or by any sculptor before him.

Collections: Cardinal Fesch (?). Henry de Montault, Paris. Susse. Victorien Sardou (1869–1908). Madame Sardou. Duveen (1911). Frick, 1939.

NOTES

1 When the statue entered The Frick Collection, Duveen Brothers provided a photograph of André's 1911 ledger entry, his letter of January 1939, the letter of 1869 from Henry de Montault to Victorien Sardou, a letter from Jean Sardou to W. L. Hatfield of 1911, and a signed statement by Hatfield concerning the negotiations for selling the *Diana* from the Sardou collection.

2 G. Giacometti, *La Vie et l'oeuvre de Houdon,* II, Paris, 1929, p. 239.

3 L. Réau, *Houdon: Sa Vie et son oeuvre,* Paris, 1964, Pt. I, p. 115.

4 According to an anonymous writer in *L'Intermédiaire des chercheurs et des curieux,* XLIX, February 29, 1904, col. 316, the statue came from the demolished residence of Cardinal Fesch.

5 No life-size reproductions by Susse are known. W. L. Hatfield, in a statement made in 1939 (see note 1), says that Susse "fit paraitre quelques petites reductions en bronze, dont certaines se trouvent encore aujourd'hui dans le commerce." According to an article by T. Revillon in *La Petite Presse* of August 30, 1869, Susse reserved the right, on selling the statue, to reproduce the bust in three sizes.

6 Much of what is known about Houdon's *Diana* in its various versions appears in documents transcribed by Réau *(op. cit.).* Giacometti's earlier book *(op. cit.),* although often perceptive, is unreliable. Documents published in recent years have rendered obsolete in some respects the accounts given by A. Michel in "Exposition Universelle de 1889: La Sculpture," *Gazette des Beaux-Arts,* 3ᵉ pér., II, 1889, pp. 281ff.; by P. Vitry in "La Diane et l'Apollon de Houdon," *Les Arts,* January 1907, p. 10; and by G. Bapst in *Diana Huntress by Jean Antoine Houdon,* Paris, 1915.

7 *Deutsche Akademie der Kunst: Jean-*

Antoine Houdon, sein Werk in Deutschland, intro. by H. Mansfeld, Berlin, 1955, p. 68. Réau, *op. cit.,* Pt. III, p. 12.

8 *Fundação Calouste Gulbenkian: Obras de Arte da Colecção Calouste Gulbenkian,* Oeiras, 1965, No. 66. Réau, *op. cit.,* Pt. II, pp. 224–33, Pt. III, p. 12.

9 R. R. Wark, *Sculpture in the Huntington Collection,* Los Angeles, 1959, p. 78, Pls. XLI, XLII. Réau, *op. cit.,* Pt. II, pp. 231–32, Pt. III, p. 13.

10 *Catalogue des sculptures, II: Temps modernes,* Paris, 1922, p. 61, No. 1353. Réau, *op. cit.,* Pt. II, pp. 231–32, Pt. III, p. 13.

11 Réau, *op. cit.,* Pt. III, p. 13.

12 *Idem,* Pt. I, p. 97, Pt. III, p. 13.

13 *Idem,* Pt. I, p. 118.

14 *Op. cit.,* II, pp. 275–76. A more detailed description of the technique is given by Lebrun and Magnier in *Nouveau Manuel complet du mouleur* (Manuels-Roret), Paris, 1910, pp. 160–68. Technical manuals in English are less explicit.

15 XII, 1955, p. 100.

16 T. Besterman, "The Terracotta Statue of Voltaire Made by Houdon for Beaumarchais," in *Voltaire Essays,* London, 1962, p. 124.

17 A. Joubin, *Catalogue des peintures et sculptures exposées dans les galeries du Musée Fabre, Montpellier,* Paris, 1926, p. 278. Réau, *op. cit.,* Pt. III, p. 19.

18 Réau, *op. cit.,* Pt. I, pp. 115, 242.

19 *Idem,* Pt. I, p. 95, No. 44.

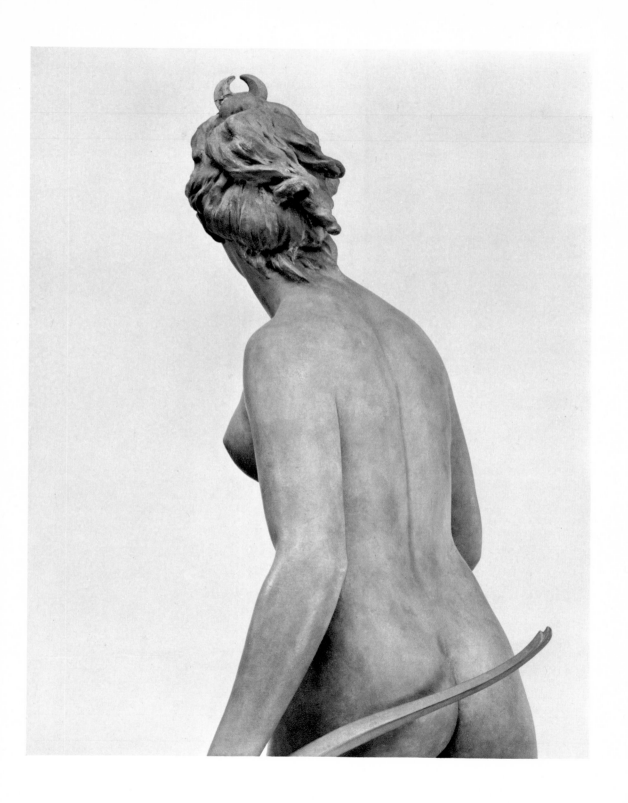

FRENCH

Eighteenth Century

Friendship (34.2.85)

Executed about 1770. Marble: H. 7⅞ in. (20 cm); L. of base 9¼ in. (23.5 cm).

Description: The young girl wears a gown which is fastened at the left shoulder and falls to reveal the right breast. Her hair is bound with two ribbons. She is seated on the ground, gazing at a heart held in her right hand, which rests on her knee. Between her right hand and her left, which lies open on the ground, runs a broad ribbon. The left foot projects beyond the shallow oval base.

Condition: The neck has been fractured and repaired. The large toe of the left foot is damaged. The base has been broken and repaired on the right, and there are several small chips in its lower edge.

A version with the left foot not projecting, but otherwise identical to the Frick example, was sold from the Bardac collection in 1927 as from the Falconet workshop,[1] and from the René Fribourg collection in 1963 (L. 10¼ in.; 26 cm) as by Boizot.[2]

Symbolic representations of Friendship[3] became popular in French art about 1750, when Madame de Pompadour let it be known that her relationship with Louis XV had been changed from that of a mistress to that of a friend. A well-known example of this theme is the statue by Falconet, exhibited in the Salon of 1765,[4] which shows Friendship as a woman bearing her heart in both hands. But there is no convincing reason for ascribing the present statuette either to Falconet or to Boizot, and the sculptor remains unidentified. On grounds of style, the statuette can be dated about 1770.

Collections: Gift of Miss Helen C. Frick, 1934.

NOTES

1 Bardac sale, Galerie Georges Petit, Paris, December 9, 1927, Lot 51.
2 Fribourg sale catalogue, VII (Pt. 2), Sotheby's, October 18, 1963, Lot 727A.
3 On the iconography of Friendship, see K. Gordon, "Madame de Pompadour, Pigalle, and the Iconography of Friendship," *Art Bulletin,* L, 1968, pp. 249 ff.
4 L. Réau, *Étienne-Maurice Falconet,* Paris, 1922, I, p. 230, Pl. XIV.

FRENCH

Probably Eighteenth Century

Head of a Boy (15.2.68)

Executed probably in the eighteenth century. Bronze: H. 14¼ in. (36.2 cm).

Description: The boy, perhaps Mars, looks downward and slightly to his left. His hair, which is bound with a ribbon, falls in curls over the forehead and in a long tress onto the right shoulder. He wears a cloak over the left shoulder and beneath the cloak a cuirass embossed with foliated scroll ornament. Above the cuirass the ruffled edge of a tunic is visible. A loop for fixing is cast solid with the bust at the back.

Condition: Dark brown lacquer over reddish bronze.

Head of a Girl (15.2.69)

Executed probably in the eighteenth century. Bronze: H. 14¼ in. (36.2 cm).

Description: The girl, perhaps Venus, looks downward and slightly to her right. Her hair, which is bound with plaits and coiled at the back, is dressed in a tightly rolled curl on the top of her head. Her neck and breast are bare, and the bust terminates in a narrow strip of twisted drapery. A loop for fixing is cast solid with the bust at the back.

Condition: Dark brown lacquer over reddish bronze.

The two busts were exhibited at Tours in 1890, when in the Rouet de Clermont collection, as works of the late seventeenth century.[1] An identical pair were catalogued in a 1919 sale of objects from the collections of Sir Philip Sassoon and Lady Rocksavage[2] as "A pair of bronze busts, of a Bacchante and a faun, by Coysevox" (later acquired by the Huntington Art Gallery, San Marino, California). Another pair were exhibited in Paris in 1960.[3] A version of the head of the girl, in the Metropolitan Museum, New York (Bequest of Mary Strong Shattuck), is marked twice with the *poinçon* of the crowned C, which, if authentic, denotes that it was sold between 1745 and 1749;[4] this version is a heavier casting and includes the top of a tunic above the drapery. Bode[5] catalogued the Frick busts, when in the Pierpont Morgan collection, as French, eighteenth century, and

identified them tentatively as Diana and Actaeon. However, the boy's armor suggests Mars, rather than Actaeon, and the absence of a crescent moon in the girl's hair suggests Venus, rather than Diana.

Collections: Rouet de Clermont. J. Pierpont Morgan, London and New York. Frick, 1915.

NOTES

1 L. Palustre, *Album de l'Exposition rétrospective de Tours,* Tours, 1891, p. 35, Pl. XVIII.
2 Sir Philip Sassoon and the Countess of Rocksavage sale, Christie's, November 26–27, 1919, Lot 84, repr. facing p. 13.
3 Paris, Musée des Arts Décoratifs, Louis XIV: Fastes et Décors, No. 751bis, lent by Madame L. Guiraud: "Buste de jeune garçon et de jeune fille."
4 J. G. Phillips, "Sculptures," *Metropolitan Museum of Art Bulletin,* XXXI, 1936, p. 6. *The French Bronze: 1500 to 1800,* Knoedler, New York, 1968, No. 62.
5 W. Bode, *The Collection of J. Pierpont Morgan: Bronzes of the Renaissance and Subsequent Periods,* Paris, 1910, I, p. xlii, II, pp. 30–31, Nos. 220, 221, Pls. CLVII, CLVIII.

FRENCH

Eighteenth Century (?)

Bust of a Young Girl (35.2.80)

Incised lightly, on the back: EB. Terracotta: H. 12⅛ in. (30.8 cm).

Description: The girl looks to her right. A ribbon cap with a lace border covers her head, allowing a fringe of curls to show in front. Over her tight bodice appears the lace edge of a shift. A scarf passes round the neck, with its ends twisted together in front.

Condition: The neck has been fractured and repaired.

Versions of the model exist in terracotta, plaster, and bronze. One plaster version passed from the Doucet collection to Duveen and then to the Hamilton Rice collection,[1] and a second plaster was sold from the collection of Mrs. Benjamin Thaw[2] and later from that of Mrs. Meyer Sassoon.[3] A terracotta version in the Albert Roze collection, Amiens, was shown in the 1928 Houdon centenary exhibition in Paris,[4] a second terracotta passed from the collection of Sir Philip Sassoon and Lady Rocksavage[5] into the Coureau collection and then to the Paris dealer Sylvain Guirard,[6] and a third terracotta was exhibited in St. Louis in 1923.[7] A bronze in the Lucas-Moreno collection was shown in the Houdon centenary exhibition in Paris.[8]

The old attribution of the model to Houdon is unacceptable and was rejected by Maclagan.[9] It had earlier been rejected by Vitry,[10] who suggested Vassé as a possible author, and by Réau,[11] but Giacometti[12] had subsequently argued in favor of the ascription to Houdon on the basis of resemblances he saw between the facture of a bronze version and that of bronzes from Houdon's workshop. As a result of Giacometti's opinion the Roze and Lucas-Moreno versions were included in the Houdon centenary exhibition in Paris, albeit cautiously catalogued.[13]

In fact, the ribbon cap and other costume details, together with the comparatively commonplace modelling and lack of expression, are uncharacteristic of

Houdon's child portraits. Vitry's proposal that Louis-Claude Vassé (1716–72) might be the author of the original model should not be excluded, although there are other eligible minor sculptors. Réau[14] saw one example inscribed *Pigalle* (an impossible attribution) and had heard of another inscribed *Masson*. At some time, probably in the late nineteenth century, the model was copiously reproduced. The Frick example must be regarded as of uncertain date. The initials EB are unexplained.

Collections: Jansen, Paris. Elsie de Wolfe (afterwards Lady Mendl). Miss Helen C. Frick, 1914. Gift of Miss Helen C. Frick, 1935.

NOTES

1 F. Ingersoll-Smouse, "Catalogue provisoire des oeuvres de Houdon conservés aux Etats-Unis," *Bulletin de la Société de l'histoire de l'art français,* 1914, p. 36.

2 Her sale (Sir Edward Brooksbank and others), June 23, 1932, Christie's, Lot 87.

3 Lord Baldwin Fund for Refugees sale, May 24–25, 1939, Christie's, Lot 136.

4 *Exposition du centenaire de Houdon,* Galeries Buvelot, Paris, 1928, p. 36, No. 20.

5 Sir Philip Sassoon and the Countess of Rocksavage sale, Christie's, November 26–27, 1919, Lot 80.

6 According to *The Frick Collection Catalogue,* VI, 1954, p. 51.

7 *St. Louis Museum: An Exhibition of French Art of the XVIII Century,* St. Louis, 1923, No. 27.

8 *Exposition du centenaire de Houdon,* No. 21.

9 E. Maclagan, in *The Frick Collection Catalogue,* VI, p. 49.

10 Jacques Doucet sale catalogue, ed. P. Vitry, Paris, June 6, 1912, II, p. 30, Lot 126.

11 L. Réau, "Notes critiques sur les expositions du centenaire de Houdon," *Bulletin de la Société de l'histoire de l'art français,* 1928, p. 328.

12 G. Giacometti, *La Vie et l'oeuvre de Houdon,* Paris, 1929, I, repr. facing p. 120, II, pp. 190–92.

13 *Exposition du centenaire de Houdon,* Nos. 20, 21.

14 *Loc. cit.* The dates of Jean-Baptiste Pigalle are 1714–85; those of François Masson are 1745–1807.

148

JOHN CHARLES LOCHÉE, Attributed to

1751–After 1791

The work of Lochée, a London sculptor who was one of the modellers employed by Josiah Wedgwood, consists of portrait busts, small portrait medallions, and copies of antique gems. Among the sitters for his portrait busts were members of the British royal family. After 1790 no sculptures by Lochée are recorded, and in 1791 he was declared bankrupt. The date of his death is unknown.

Bust of a Lady, Perhaps Mrs. Mary Robinson (15.2.74)

Executed probably between 1775 and 1790. Marble: H., including base, 32 in. (81.3 cm).

Description: The sitter looks to her right. Her hair is dressed in curls and bound with a ribbon. Ringlets fall over her shoulders. Under a fur-lined cloak she wears a gown edged at the neck with a soft frill. An oval medallion bearing the letters M and R interlaced is suspended from her neck by a twisted ribbon. The drapery is gathered in a knot below the breast and falls over the polygonal molded base, which is carved in one with the bust.

Condition: There are scattered flaws in the marble, most noticeably in the lower portion of the knotted drapery in front of the base and on the lower left cheek. There is a chip in the drapery over the right arm.

When in the Pierpont Morgan collection, the bust was identified as a portrait of Madame Roland by Augustin Pajou.[1] In a draft entry for *The Frick Collection Catalogue* of 1953–54, Maclagan rejected this identification of the subject but proposed no alternative; the bust was omitted from the catalogue. The features of Marie-Jeanne Roland, the leader of the Girondists, as recorded in her portraits, do not in fact resemble those of the bust at all closely;[2] furthermore, the subject of the bust, to judge from her fur-lined cloak and her hair style, appears to be a woman of fashion. Maclagan also rightly rejected the ascription to Pajou, but added that no more appropriate name had been suggested. Busts by Pajou are not shaped in the manner of the present bust and they never terminate in bunched drapery falling over the base; nor does Pajou treat the hair of his female subjects in such elaborate detail.

149

There are, however, striking analogies to the present work in busts by John Charles Lochée,[3] a London sculptor, presumably of French extraction, whose style in portrait busts had not been identified at the time when Maclagan's catalogue entry was prepared. Lochée's busts taper slowly inward from below the shoulder and the truncations are swathed in drapery. He is partial to specific details of costume and to the rendering of a medallion suspended from a ribbon. The hair or wig is carved meticulously. Although his busts date from the last quarter of the eighteenth century, their appearance is rococo rather than neoclassical. None of those so far recognized is signed.

If the attribution to Lochée is accepted, the subject must be sought in London between about 1775 and 1790. Assuming that the cipher on the medallion gives her initials, no more likely candidate can be suggested than the actress and writer Mrs. Mary Robinson (1758–1800), known among her contemporaries as "Perdita." She attracted the notice of the Prince of Wales (later George IV) when she was playing the role of Perdita in *A Winter's Tale* in 1778, and for a short time she became his mistress. She left the stage in 1780. Mrs. Robinson's first poems were published in 1775. These were followed by more poems, by plays, novels, and pamphlets, and by her memoirs, which were published posthumously in 1801.[4]

That Mrs. Robinson employed the cipher MR on her carriage is vouched for by Laetitia Matilda Hawkins,[5] who lived in the same street in about 1780: "Her chariot had been set out in the best style, and she had opened to Sherwin all the plan of the pretty basket of five round flowers, which surmounted the rose-wreath, disposed into M.R; she had brought him to confess that, *at a distance,* this basket *did* deceive the eye into the notion of a five-pearled coronet." In a caricature of 1782,[6] when Mrs. Robinson was believed to have become the mistress of Charles James Fox, she is shown riding with him in her phaeton, on which is a wreath encircling the initials MR.

If the bust does represent Mrs. Robinson, a date in the early 1780s is probable, as those were the days of both her prosperity and her notoriety. It is perhaps worth mentioning that among the very few sitters for busts known to be by Lochée are the Prince of Wales, his brother the Duke of York, who was present at the early assignations with Mrs. Robinson, and Sheridan, her theatrical manager and close friend.

Nevertheless, it cannot be argued that there is a close resemblance between the

150

bust and the painted portraits of Mrs. Robinson, which include works by Reynolds, Gainsborough, Romney, Cosway, and Engleheart.[7] In particular, the shape of the nose in the profile portrait by Reynolds is markedly dissimilar. If, therefore, the bust was intended to represent Mrs. Robinson, it must certainly be judged a poor likeness, and the identification remains doubtful.

Exhibited: New York, Metropolitan Museum, 1914, Morgan Collection, lent by the J. Pierpont Morgan Estate.

Collections: J. Pierpont Morgan, London and New York. Frick, 1915.

NOTES

1 *Guide to the Loan Exhibition of the J. Pierpont Morgan Collection,* Metropolitan Museum, New York, 1914, p. 114.

2 Portraits of Madame Roland are reproduced in: I. A. Taylor, *Life of Madame Roland,* London, 1911; U. Pope-Hennessy, *Madame Roland. A study in revolution,* London, 1917; M. Clemenceau-Jacquemaire, *Vie de Madame Roland,* Paris, 1929. Her appearance can probably be best judged from the painting by Heinsius at Versailles (Taylor, *op. cit.,* frontispiece) and the profile engraving by Gaucher reproduced in W. von Seidlitz, *Allgemeines historisches Porträtwerk,* XII, Munich, 1890, Pl. 14. A bust which is widely considered to represent Madame Roland is discussed by L. Réau in "L'Inconnue du Musée de Nevers," *Bulletin de la Société de l'histoire de l'art français,* 1929, p. 196.

3 For the life and work of Lochée, see: T. Hodgkinson, "John Lochée, Portrait Sculptor," in *Victoria and Albert Museum Yearbook,* I, 1969, pp. 152–60; R. Gunnis, *Dictionary of British Sculptors: 1660–1851,* London, 1954, p. 241.

4 *Memoirs of the late Mrs. Robinson written by herself,* London, 1801. For her life, see also:

Dictionary of National Biography, ed. S. Lee, XVII, London, 1909, p. 30; M. Steen, *The Lost One,* London, 1937; S. V. Makower, *Perdita: a romance in biography,* London, 1908. The Steen and Makower biographies are illustrated with portraits.

5 L. M. Hawkins, *Memoirs, anecdotes, facts and opinions, collected and preserved by Laetitia Matilda Hawkins,* II, London, 1824, pp. 30–31. The Sherwin referred to in the quotation is the engraver J. K. Sherwin.

6 M. George, *British Museum: Catalogue of political and personal satires, V: 1771–83,* London, 1935, p. 645, No. 6117. The print, by Colley, was published by W. Richardson in 1782; its title is "Perdito and Perdita—or—the Man and the Woman of the People."

7 The principal portraits are the Gainsborough, Reynolds (profile), and Romney in the Wallace Collection, London, and the Reynolds at Waddesdon Manor. See: *Wallace Collection Catalogues: Pictures and Drawings,* London, 1968, Nos. P 42, P 45, and P 37; E. Waterhouse, *The James A. de Rothschild Collection at Waddesdon Manor: Paintings,* Fribourg, 1967, No. 28.

FRENCH (?)

Nineteenth Century

Louis XIV (?) (20.2.66)

Executed in the late nineteenth century. Marble: H. of bust 30½ in. (77.5 cm); H. of stand 9¾ in. (24.8 cm).

Description: The subject looks to his left. The balls of the eyes are blank. He wears a high-crowned, flowing wig, with copious ringlets falling over the shoulders. Under his cloak, which is fastened with a brooch on the right shoulder, is visible the top of a cuirass over a tunic. The wig is not fully carved in back.

Condition: The marble is coarse and flecked. The surface is weathered.

Although this bust was formerly ascribed to Coysevox, its authenticity has been doubted for many years. Gaston Brière[1] remarked in 1950 on its resemblance to a bust of Louis XIV in the Louvre collection (Chauchard Bequest; now housed in the Hôtel de la Monnaie), which is thought to date from the late nineteenth century. The features of the Monnaie bust are more rounded, the head is turned rather less, and the brooch is somewhat different, but its quadrangular stand decorated with a cartouche is similar to that which supports the Frick bust. The two busts seem to come from the same workshop.

Collections: Frick, 1920 (?).[2]

NOTES

1 Letter to The Frick Collection, July 20, 1950.
2 No documentary record of the date of acquisition, or of the earlier history of the bust, has been found. The bust may have been acquired during the last years of Mr. Frick's life, in 1918 or 1919.

UNIDENTIFIED SCULPTURE

UNIDENTIFIED

Nineteenth Century (?)

Reclining Antelope (?) (16.2.33)

Bronze: H. 11⅜ in. (29 cm); L. 15¼ in. (38.8 cm).

Description: The animal, perhaps an antelope (see below), reclines with forelegs folded beneath it. It scratches its neck with the right hind foot, and its head is turned slightly to its right. The animal is cast in one with the irregular naturalistic base. The back is not fully worked up, and at the base has been left almost in the rough.

Condition: Smooth dark brown bronze mottled with a darker color. The inside of the animal is partly filled with an ashen gray deposit.

The bronze was regarded in the Kann collection[1] and by Bode[2] as North Italian work of the sixteenth century. This designation is retained in the guide to the 1914–16 exhibition of the Morgan collection,[3] and by Swarzenski,[4] who observes that "the *Figure of a Gazelle* is such a happy creation that any comment about its artistic beauty is superfluous. The classification of North Italian, 16th century is correct. The general character of the bronze points to Northeastern Italy." Maclagan,[5] noting the "marked Oriental affinities of the model," observes that "it can at any rate hardly be earlier, and a North Italian origin seems as likely as any other." The editors of *The Frick Collection Catalogue*[6] regard it as "almost certainly inspired by an Eastern original, although it is almost as certainly of North Italian origin," and compare it with the well-known seventh century stone carving of a *Scratching Deer* at Mamallapuram (South India).

There are no related North Italian bronzes. According to a report from the British Museum (Natural History), the bronze does not represent any known species of deer, and the head and ears are bovine, the nearest parallel being a young bull bantin, sometimes found in India but more commonly in Burma, Malaya, and Java. The bronze is seemingly a pastiche of an Oriental, probably Indian, motif, cast in Europe or in a Europeanized art school in Southeast Asia. In either event it is likely, despite its undoubted charm, to date from no earlier

159

than the mid-nineteenth century. The possibility of a dating in the sixteenth century must, for technical and other reasons, be ruled out.

Exhibited: London, Victoria and Albert Museum, 1909–12, No. 1334, lent by J. Pierpont Morgan. New York, Metropolitan Museum, Morgan Collection, 1914–16, No. 1577, lent by the J. Pierpont Morgan Estate.

Collections: Rodolphe Kann, Paris. J. Pierpont Morgan, London and New York. Duveen. Frick, 1916.

NOTES

1 *Catalogue de la collection Rodolphe Kann: Objets d'art,* Paris, 1907, I, p. 47, No. 58.
2 W. Bode, *Collection of J. Pierpont Morgan: Bronzes of the Renaissance and Subsequent Periods,* Paris, 1910, II, p. 26, No. 201, Pl. CXXXVIII.
3 *Guide to the Loan Exhibition of the J. Pierpont Morgan Collection,* Metropolitan Museum, New York, 1914, p. 48.
4 G. Swarzenski, in *Duveen Sculpture in Public Collections of America,* New York, 1944, No. 224.
5 E. Maclagan, in *The Frick Collection Catalogue,* V, 1953, pp. 52–53.
6 *Loc. cit.*

INDICES

INDEX OF SCULPTORS

165

INDEX OF SUBJECTS

FIGURES AND HEADS (MISCELLANEOUS)

NEW TESTAMENT

OLD TESTAMENT

PORTRAITS

PORTRAITS, UNIDENTIFIED

SAINTS AND ANGELS

UTENSILS

CONCORDANCE OF CHANGES OF ATTRIBUTION AND TITLE

Folio Catalogue of 1953–54

Present Catalogue

ASPETTI, Tiziano
Perseus

ASPETTI, Tiziano
Mars

BELLANO, Bartolomeo, Workshop of
The Young David

BELLANO, Bartolomeo, After

BERTOLDO DI GIOVANNI
Hercules

BERTOLDO DI GIOVANNI, Style of

BOLOGNA, Giovanni
Virtue Overcoming Vice

SOLDANI, Massimiliano
Virtue Triumphant Over Vice

BOLOGNA, Giovanni, Follower of
A Triton Blowing a Trumpet

LORENZI, Battista, Attributed to

BORDONI, Francesco
Hercules and the Hydra

FRENCH, Middle of the Seventeenth
Century

CLODION
Cupid and Psyche: The Embrace

CLODION
Zephyrus and Flora

DANIELE DA VOLTERRA
Samson and the Philistines

MICHELANGELO BUONARROTI, After
Samson and Two Philistines

DERBAIS, Jérome
Marshal Turenne

COYSEVOX (?), Antoine

FLORENCE, School of
Virtue Triumphant Over Vice

ROMAN, Late Sixteenth Century
Virtue Overcoming Vice

173

FLORENTINE or PADUAN SCHOOL, Fifteenth Century
The Christ Child

FRANCE, School of
Venus

FRANCESCO DI GIORGIO
Hercules in Repose

GERMAN SCHOOL (?), Circa 1600
Venus

ITALIAN SCHOOL, Late Seventeenth Century
Head of a Faun

LEONE LEONI
Bust of Antonio Galli

MULTSCHER, Hans
Reliquary Bust of a Saint
(Saint Katherine?)

NORTHERN ITALY, School of
Inkstand in the Form of a Casket

NORTHERN ITALY, School of, Sixteenth Century
Reclining Antelope

PADUA, School of, Late Fifteenth Century
Queen Tomyris with the Head of Cyrus

PADUA, School of, Early Sixteenth Century
An Infant Faun

ITALIAN, Nineteenth Century (?)
Seated Child

LORENZI, Stoldo, After
Marine Nymph

FLORENTINE, Early Sixteenth Century

NETHERLANDISH, Seventeenth Century

SOLDANI, Massimiliano, Style of

BRANDANI, Federico

MULTSCHER, Hans, Attributed to

SEVERO DA RAVENNA, After
Casket

UNIDENTIFIED, Nineteenth Century (?)
Reclining Antelope (?)

SEVERO DA RAVENNA

GRAS, Caspar

PADUA, School of, Early Sixteenth Century
Meleager (or Adonis)

BANDINI, Giovanni
Adonis

PADUA, School of
The Spinario

SEVERO DA RAVENNA, Workshop of

POLLAIUOLO, Antonio del
Marsyas

POLLAJUOLO, Antonio, Style of

POLLAIUOLO, Follower of,
Late Fifteenth Century
Paris

NUREMBERG, First Half of the
Sixteenth Century

REICHLE, Hans
Two Lamps: Harpies Bestriding
Dolphins

FLORENTINE, Second Half of the
Sixteenth Century

RICCIO
The Fugitive (Marsyas?)

RICCIO
Naked Youth with Raised Left Arm

RICCIO
A Hand Bell

GRANDI, Gian Girolamo

RICCIO
Susanna

RICCIO, Attributed to
Naked Female Figure

RICCIO, School of
Inkstand: Atlas Supporting the Globe
of Heaven

RICCIO, Workshop of

RICCIO, School of
Inkstand with Marsyas Bound

SEVERO DA RAVENNA
Triangular Lamp with a Bound Satyr

RICCIO, School of
A Warrior on Horseback

RICCIO, Workshop of

RICCIO, Workshop of
Triton and Nereid

RICCIO

RICCIO, Workshop of,
    Early Sixteenth Century
    Satyr Mother with a Child

ROME, School of, Circa 1450
    Symbolic She-Wolf

SANT'AGATA, Francesco da
    A Faun Playing the Flute

SANT'AGATA, Francesco da
    Youth with Raised Hands

SIENA, School of, Late Fifteenth Century
    Symbolic She-Wolf

VISCHER, Hans
    Eve

VITTORIA, Alessandro, Follower of, Late
    Seventeenth or Early Eighteenth Century
    A Firedog with a Figure of Jupiter
    A Firedog with a Figure of Venus

VOLTERRA, Daniele da,
    see DANIELE DA VOLTERRA

VRIES, Adriaen de
    Triton and Nereid

VRIES, Adriaen de, After
    Nessus and Dejaneira

NUREMBERG, Last Quarter of the
    Sixteenth Century

PADUAN (?), Early Sixteenth Century

CAMELIO

VENETIAN, Early Sixteenth Century

ITALIAN, First Half of the Sixteenth
    Century

GRUPELLO, Gabriel

VENETIAN, Late Eighteenth or Early
    Nineteenth Century

GERHARD, Hubert, Attributed to

VRIES, Adriaen de, Attributed to

SCULPTURE NOT INCLUDED IN THE FOLIO CATALOGUE OF 1953–54